Library Concourse,
University of East Anglia
6–28 October 1979

Edvard Munch
AND HIS LITERARY ASSOCIATES

AN EXHIBITION OF
PRINTS BOOKS AND DOCUMENTS
ARRANGED BY CARLA LATHE

Hatton Gallery,
University of Newcastle upon Tyne
5–30 November 1979

Crawford Centre for the Arts,
University of St. Andrews
8 December 1979 – 6 January 1980

PREFACE AND ACKNOWLEDGEMENTS

EDVARD MUNCH AND HIS LITERARY ASSOCIATES is conceived as a didactic exhibition in the best sense of the word. Its focal point is a series of original prints by Munch which speak to us directly and need no intermediary. Munch's art was however stimulated and influenced by the wider artistic and literary movement around the turn of the century and by his friendship with poets and writers in Scandinavia, in Germany and in France. An understanding of this will heighten our appreciation of Munch's art without detracting from the aesthetic and emotional impact which it makes on us. The exhibition seeks to demonstrate this by showing a range of contemporary material – books, articles, poems which reflect the intellectual environment within which the great Norwegian artist worked and on which he frequently drew for inspiration.

This catalogue itself is conceived as a key to this world as well as a record of the exhibition. It is the work of Dr. Carla Lathe who also selected and arranged the material shown and whose expertise and enthusiasm created the exhibition. Her work was supported by a grant from the British Academy. Help in the preparation and mounting of the exhibition was given by the staff of the University Library, the Audio-Visual Centre, the School of Fine Art and Music and the Scandinavian Sector of the School of Modern Languages and European History.

Munch's work is relatively unknown in Britain and only comparatively little of his graphic work is represented in public or private collections. Without the willingness of the Munch Museum in Oslo to lend the original prints shown here the exhibition could never have been mounted. We are very grateful to them for their cooperation and to Mr. Arne Eggum, the Chief Curator of the Museum, who showed great interest in the project.

The Norwegian Cultural Attache in London, Mr. Torbjørn Støverud also encouraged the venture from the beginning and we are deeply appreciative of this and of the financial contributions towards the production of the catalogue which we received from the Norwegian Embassy and from the Norwegian Ministry of Foreign Affairs.

The exhibition has been mounted to coincide with the 45th Norfolk and Norwich Triennial Festival and it complements the latter's musical themes. The Festival Committee very generously made a grant towards the cost of mounting this exhibition. To them, to the Anglo-Norse Society who also supported the exhibition financially and to Air Anglia, who very kindly agreed to transport the prints from Norway and fly them back there free of charge, our sincere thanks are due. Our thanks are also due to Dr. James Milner, Curator of the Hatton Gallery,

University of Newcastle and to Mrs. Jennifer Wilson, Director of the Crawford Centre for the Arts, University of St. Andrews for the interest which they showed in the exhibition and for their contribution towards the cost of mounting it. Without such generous support which supplemented the contribution from the Art Exhibition Fund through which the University regularly supports exhibitions in the Library Concourse our venture could not have succeeded.

W.L. GUTTSMAN,
Librarian,
University of East Anglia

LIST OF LENDERS

Munch Museum, Oslo Municipal Art Collections
Cambridge University Library
Miss Charlotte Carstairs
Copenhagen University Library
Dr. Carla Lathe
Mr. Torbjørn Støverud
The Taylor Institution, Oxford
University of East Anglia Library
University College London Library

ISBN 0 902876 04

Published by the Library, University of East Anglia, Norwich, England.

© Text: Carla Lathe. Photographs: Munch Museum, British Library, Lillehammer Art Gallery, Rasmus Meyer Collection, Bergen Municipal Art Collections.

Catalogue design by Richard Johnson.

EDVARD MUNCH AND HIS LITERARY ASSOCIATES: AN ESSAY ON THE INTERPRETATION OF ART AND LITERATURE AROUND THE TURN OF THE CENTURY

1. Sigbjørn Obstfelder, 1896, lithograph OKK G/L 220

Edvard Munch was one of the most powerful and innovatory artists of the early modern period. Throughout his long life, 1863-1944, he remained an independent figure and never belonged to any one 'school' of art. But he had many friends, as is obvious from his portraits of them. The English composer Delius, the German critic Meier-Graefe and the Polish writer Przybyszewski were just a few of the close friends who helped Munch to arrange exhibitions in different countries in Europe. His broad-minded attitudes and ability to express a profound insight into human nature created a channel for artistic communication which has both disturbed and pleased ever since the 1880s.

Munch is traditionally known as an artist who expressed his own emotions in his art. However, it is a mistake to believe that he produced simply autobiographical paintings, dashing them off without any conscious effort. He was interested and curious about other people, so much so that he would sit in a railway station just to watch the faces and gestures around him. Above all he was able to express other people's emotions and to touch a submerged but common vein of human experience. He used his eyes and paintbrush to create a vivid, moving art.

Munch liked to give the impression that he painted in quick moments of inspiration or in a trance-like state. This may have happened occasionally later in his life, but in the early years his work was far from being automatic. He toiled for years on paintings like **The Scream** and **The Sick Child** before he found an image that satisfied him. If any of the paintings were based on personal experience, there was a considerable interval of time and effort between the original sensation and the process of recreating it. He moreover repeated his images and painted groups on the same theme. This suggests that he developed a subject with conscious care.

People who knew Munch and who understood his native language, did not find him morbid. Paul Gauguin's son, Pola, for example wrote in his book on Munch's prints (1946):

> That Munch opted for loneliness has nothing to do with melancholy. Because Munch was not a melancholic, he was much too close to life and in search of life to become a mournful brooder. When he treated melancholy in some of his works, it was always close friends, Obstfelder, for example, whom he had in mind and for whom he felt sympathy. But seen as a whole his art points to an affirmative view of life and much humour, which not infrequently can be quite malicious.

Who were Obstfelder and the other close friends whom Gauguin thought were in Munch's mind when he developed his images of melancholy? They were his literary associates. It was they who fostered in Munch the more visionary and introspective branch of his art. A look at their literature and at what they wrote about Munch gives us important secondary information about the philosophical background to many of his pictures. While using his own memories, he also used his friends' features, predicaments, ideas and creative writing. He himself said that he had found material for several pictures in Obstfelder's poems and that he had begun to sketch **The Scream** after reading Obstfelder's poem 'I see'.[1] Munch's sketches on the theme of **Despair** may well have been intended as illustrations for this poem's mood of fear and isolation (ill. 2). He had tried to sketch and write about his memory of a sense of loneliness once at sunset early in 1892, but the request for a book illustration made him develop a more concentrated and expressive composition, which he used for his paintings **Despair** and **The Scream** (cat. 96-100).

2. Sketches for **Despair**, 1892 OKK T 129-38

One of the reasons why Munch was drawn to writers was that he considered himself a poet. He wrote extensively himself but published little. Much of his writing is related to experiences he projected in his pictures, and he re-wrote the texts in several versions. He referred to his writing as his 'spiritual diary', and it included his personal memories, his creative fantasies, and his ideas about art, religion and life. The variations in his texts, from diary notes to aphorisms and prose poems, suggest that he was not trying to document his past so much as to explore impressions which lingered in his mind and which he wanted to use in different ways for his creative art. The Munch Museum in Oslo has albums with his prints and related texts which he pasted together in about 1915 and 1929. In 1904-8 he wrote a satirical play and in 1909 he published texts below the lithographs in his album **Alpha and Omega**.

Literature, history and art had been important in Munch's home, which had little material wealth or comfort. His father was a doctor, but should have been a writer, according to his son.[2] Munch's aunt, brother and sisters were all talented in drawing and they used to create their own illustrations for the books and magazines they read. As his exceptional gift for art developed, the literary material which Munch found stimulating included the most modern books of his day. He also enjoyed performances of music and drama, and when he arrived in Paris for his first brief study trip in 1885, he went to the theatre before he looked at a single picture there (Brev 46). Many of his paintings convey dramatic movement. An awareness of his receptivity to literature and pleasure in creativity makes it easier to see his art and writing in perspective.

The exhibition which illustrates Munch's association with writers is mainly from the 1890s and reflects the exposure of death and love which was characteristic of many of his friends. The writers often worked under difficult conditions and faced fierce hostility on account of the subjects they chose to treat. Their books were repeatedly banned by the censors and, however democratic their intentions, they depended for support on each other rather than on a wide reading public. It was from these writers and from painters with literary sympathies that Munch received most encouragement in the 1880s and 1890s.

The best of the Norwegian poets of his generation was Obstfelder (ill.1), whose work Munch planned to illustrate in 1892. Munch's paintings of the period are very similar to the imagery and sentiment of Obstfelder's poems, for example his 'Christmas Eve':

> I roamed alone on the streets
> and listened to children's songs.
> I sat down on the steps
> and thought of my dead mother.

And I went out into the fields –
out – among the stars.
My shadow slid over the shadows
of trees with skeleton arms.

The images of the dead mother, the stars and shadows in the night, the trees with dead branches recur in Munch's paintings of the 1890s and mark a contrast to the emphasis on luxurious growth in nature which was typical of the **art nouveau** of the period. (ill.3 and 21). Like the poets he used images from nature as agents in the exposure of inner life and imagination.

Time and again Munch's early critics distinguished him from contemporary painters who created idyllic scenes in minute details or who tried to express a more primitive style of life. The German critic Franz Servaes in 1894 argued that there was a fundamental difference between the intuitive second sight of Munch's visions and the more external escapism of other painters, like Gauguin. He wrote that Munch 'does not need to paint peasants or centaurs or boys of paradise and he does not need to go to Tahiti to see and experience the primitive element in human nature. He carries within him his own Tahiti'.[3] Not only his presentation of figures but also his landscapes and paintings of the seashore seemed to critics to reveal the imaginative faculty which people expected in literature but not in visual art. One reviewer remarked that the painting **Mystic Shore** showed that 'Munch simply never paints from nature – he works like a writer who does not sit down in front of the sea either when he wants to render a sea mood with words which have a rhythmic effect' (cat.105).

Munch's literary associates were among the first to recognize his calibre as a painter. They pointed out that an art which expressed feelings, memories, dreams and fantasy was just as legitimate as the visual recreation of external reality. In the 1890s Przybyszewski, Meier-Graefe and Obstfelder had no hesitation in describing Munch as a genius, even though there were critics, particularly among aspiring psychiatrists, who proclaimed him mad (cat. 108). Munch himself liked to explain his art as an attempt to express the inconsistencies he discovered in himself, but a glance at his prints shows his control of his subject. It was his effort to express fundamental aspects of life as directly as possible that distanced him from the conventional art market and united him with the most modern writers of his day.

3. **The Lonely One**, 1892, sketch for vignette for book of poems, OKK T 129 p.21

THE CHRISTIANIA BOHEMIANS:
KROHG AND JAEGER

4. **Christiania Bohême I**, 1895, etching OKK G/r 9

'When will someone describe that Bohemian period, who will do it? It would have to be a Dostoyevsky or a mixture of Krohg, Jaeger and possibly myself, to be capable of describing the Russian period in the Siberian town which Oslo then was and still is.'

(Munch to Pola Gauguin)

The friends who were most significant to Munch in the 1880s, when he began his painting career, were known as 'the Christiania Bohemians'. Christiania was the name for Oslo at the time, and the group was labelled as Bohemians after the publication of Hans Jaeger's novel **From the Christiania Bohème** in 1885 (cat. 20). The group is remembered in particular for its 9 commandments, published in the last issue of the newspaper **The Impressionist** (cat. 6). The commandments included '1. You shall write your autobiography. 2. You shall sever your family roots. 9. You *shall* take your own life.' The defiant subjectivity points to a bitterness and zeal in exposing personal feelings which was quite different from the French concept of impressionism.

Characteristic of the Christiania Bohemians was that in their paintings and books they attempted to show how a person could be affected by distress and give an insight into the lives of the unsuccessful and unfortunate. The first painter to guide Munch in this direction was his part-time teacher Christian Krohg, who was also a writer and astute journalist. Krohg may have encouraged Munch to write and illustrate his own texts, as he did. The two men were often together when Krohg wrote his novel **Albertine** about the tragic life of a seamstress who became a prostitute after being raped by a policeman. (cat. 21) Krohg said it was a true story. His book was banned by the censor but Krohg in 1887 exhibited a large painting illustrating a scene in the novel, and Munch later said that he had painted one of the women on the canvas.

As a painter, Munch could learn from Krohg the use of photographs. He responded to Krohg's handling of light and compositional devices of a strong diagonal and sectional view of his subjects, leaving them cut off at the edges. An example of this is **A Corner of my Studio**, which Krohg painted early in 1885, and in which he showed the actress Constance Bruun together with three painters, of whom the one on the left was Munch (cat. 2 and ill. 34).

Although Krohg was one of the main Norwegian exponents of naturalism in art and literature, he believed that his own generation's attention to detail and objectivity was old-fashioned and ineffective in giving a true impression of the age. While art critics constantly complained that Munch's pictures looked unfinished, Krohg wrote in 1889 that Munch succeeded in expressing what seemed important to him and in subordinating everything else, which was why he showed

an advance on the previous generation of painters. Krohg described Munch as the most promising and modern painter in Norway, in fact Norway's only **impressionist** (cat. 3).

Krohg applied the term 'impressionism' to both literature and art, and thought that it should aim to give a subjective, compelling and truthful representation of modern life. Manet, Böcklin and Klinger in his opinion were the painters of the movement, Guy de Maupassant and Hans Jaeger the writers. Fantasy, intensity of feeling and clarity of communication were the qualities Krohg recommended for modern painters in his lectures and articles. He predicted that the next generation would project its own moods and feelings, and he argued that art should not impress but move people. In 1888 he wrote on the subject of modern art, 'your duty is to take the stubborn public by the collar and make it stop to look at what you want to show'.[4]

Munch's engravings **The Day After, Christiania Bohème I** and **Tête-à-tête** (cat. 31, 1, 32), are based on paintings in which he expressed the features and situations he had observed around him in the 1880s. Some of the paintings are lost, but the engravings with their bottles and glasses recreate the visual and dramatic material in Munch's artistic environment. **The Day After** was originally painted in 1885-6, while Krohg was writing his book about prostitutes. **Tête-à-tête** and **Christiania Bohème I**, evoke the atmosphere of intimate conversations with smoke and drink in cheap lodgings which Krohg painted in **A Corner of my Studio** and which Jaeger described in his book **From the Christiania Bohème**. The imprecise hands and the shadow on the left of Munch's engraving **Christiania Bohème I** are typical of his projection of mood and psychic atmosphere. He here portrayed himself on the left, smoking, together with three friends, of whom one was the writer Axel Maurer. (ill.4)

The leader of the bohemian group was the writer Hans Jaeger (ill.5). He was a powerful, sometimes fanatical, speaker in debates and usually won his arguments. A naturalist and determinist, he came into conflict with the Establishment because he campaigned for sexual candour and permissiveness for women as well as for men. Jaeger despised religious and social morality as irrational and recommended free love in place of marriage, maintaining that couples should separate when they tired of each other. He repeatedly described love as a bird of prey in his novel **From the Christiania Bohème** (1885): 'when it comes, [love] descends on us like a bird of prey on its victim. We do not have control of it.' (vol. 2, XXII)

Jaeger's book gave Munch a precedent for the vexed treatment of love which would serve as a point of departure for a whole series of paintings in the 1890s. Munch admired Jaeger's novel and listed it in February 1892 as one of the four books in his small libary. The book must have been an important influence on the way Munch wrote fragments of his autobiography in 1890-2, and traced his personality to his background. He moreover appears to have shared Jaeger's view that love was a destructive force, and in 1893-4 similarly showed men being attacked by love in the form of a vampire or harpy. He drew a variation of the image to illustrate Strindberg's play **Simoom** in 1898 (cat. 60). A problem which recurs in the books of Jaeger and Strindberg is a man's inablity to sustain a sexual relationship. In presenting the problem as material for creative writing, they touched

5. Hans Jaeger, 1896, lithograph OKK G/I 218

on subjects which were taboo in society, and which the observant Munch turned into expressive pictures.

Like Strindberg, Jaeger was convinced that sexual abstinence was harmful after he had read a Danish translation of a book published anonymously by a Scottish doctor, George Drysdale, **The Elements of Social Science; or Physical, Sexual and Natural Religion. An exposition of the cause and only cure of the three primary social evils: poverty, prostitution, and celibacy.** The naturalist literature of Munch's associates derived many of its theories on human behaviour from contemporary medical ideas and attempted to demonstrate them in literary case histories. Jaeger in his novel tried to prove that young men could become impotent or be driven to suicide if they continued to observe Christian and social morals.

Jaeger encouraged his friends to write their autobiographies with a pessimistic, anti-social bias. He wrote in the foreword to **From the Christiania Bohême** that a naturalist, determinist author would investigate the lives of social outcasts such as criminals, prostitutes and young bohemians whose energy and individuality were doomed to be destroyed by society. His book opened with the line 'I was ill', and after a description of how he nearly died in childhood, his fictional ego continues to describe his lonely, frustrated life, and that of another young man who kills himself. The emphasis is on deprivation and on a grim determinism. When the narrator reads philosophy, he reflects that he could be no more than a spectator in a new, free society because his seeds of life had been killed long ago 'and death does not return what it has once gripped with its skeleton hand ... I could not **live** any more.' (vol. 2, XXVII) When the narrator's friend plans to commit suicide, he feels scorned by the people around him. In his hallucination their faces 'flowed together in front of him into a single, large, revolting hovering smile.' (vol. 2, XXIII) The sense of doom in these images can be compared with Munch's **Self-portrait with skeleton arm** (cat. 4) and the surrealist faces he painted in **Evening on Karl Johan** in 1892.

The Scottish doctor who influenced Jaeger's novel had complained of the profound ignorance of moralists on sexual matters and of the morbid delicacy which forbade discussion of the subject. Jaeger made a point of being frank, and exceeded the limits of the permissible in 1885. As a consequence he was prosecuted and sentenced to prison for passages which were considered obscene and blasphemous. He smuggled about 300 copies to Sweden under another title, for which he was again sentenced to prison. Munch was close to Jaeger in the days preceding both terms in prison; he provided Jaeger with a picture to hang in his cell the first time, and on the night before Jaeger went to serve his second term in 1888, Munch wrote to the author Arne Garborg, 'I am now sitting in the Grand [Café] together with Hans Jaeger who is to be locked up tomorrow.' (OUB Brevs. 40) The next day accompanied Jaeger to the prison.

Munch appears to have been torn between the Christiania Bohemians and his pious family. He questioned his family's faith, and merged their protestant pietism with his own creation of psychic perception, based on visual experience. Because he remained emotionally tied to his family, he was something of an outsider in Jaeger's circle. Munch was sensitive where the others tended to be didactic and polemical, but he was persuaded by Jaeger that the exposure of suffering in creative art would open people's eyes to an underlying reality in life. He painted **The Sick Child** while he was a friend of Jaeger and Krohg. As a young man he had accompanied his father on visits to hospital and to patients in the poor district of Oslo, and from these visits, as well as from the experience of illness in his family, he gained considerable insight into suffering.

In later life Munch stressed that his association with the bohemians had been crucial for his development as an artist. Although he was not a political activist like Jaeger and was not as involved with social reform as Krohg, he shared their conviction that art should express human concerns. It was as an artist that he looked at the people around him. The French art critic Natanson observed that Christiania Bohême was for Munch a starting-point, where he arranged drinkers at a table for the pleasure of displaying beautiful tones of colour. (cat. 101) Munch also used his literary friends as models for more psychological pictures, for example **Melancholy**. Munch drew the first sketch in a notebook in which he described the love affairs of the Bohemians, and it refers to the predicament of Jappe Nilssen; Nilssen had been rejected for another by one of the 'liberated' women in the Christiania Bohême group (cat. 7). In developing the picture from his observation of a friend's distress, Munch followed the advice of Krohg and Jaeger to express intense human feelings.

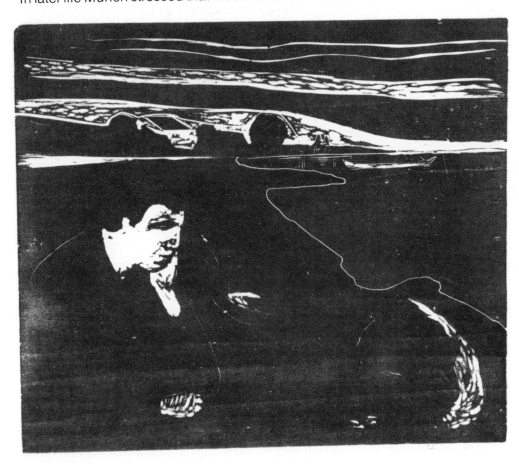

6. **Melancholy,** 1896, woodcut, OKK G/t 571

POEMS AND PICTURES ON THE THEME OF MELANCHOLY AND DESPAIR

Munch in 1890-2 wrote extensively and sometimes combined texts and illustrations on the same page (cat. 97). The main stimulus to develop his writing and related drawings into vivid images came from his association with symbolist poets, three of whom asked him to provide illustrations for their poems. Although only one frontispiece was actually printed, Munch's notebooks show drafts for a number of others which developed into images of loneliness and despair (ill.2-3). His friends' poems, their ideas and reactions to his paintings, filtered into his own cycle of writing, sketching, painting and, after 1894, printing. He needed to draw bold designs for book illustrations, and the literature he was supposed to illuminate was an important

contributing factor to the pictures of loneliness, fear and love which he developed in the 1890s.

As a student in Paris in 1889-1890, Munch and the Danish poet Emanuel Goldstein wrote literary notes together in which they developed a more concentrated version of the subjective, psychological impressionism encouraged by Krohg and Jaeger in the 1880s. Munch and Goldstein wrote with the intention of producing vibrations of feeling in the reader, and they explored moods and lingering memories in an attempt to evoke subconscious awareness. They planned to publish together a journal for art and literature.

Munch enjoyed reading a slim book of Goldstein's poems which present love as a poisonous spell and evoke a man's feelings of pain and separation after the relationship is terminated. Some of Munch's subsequent pictures like **Separation** (ill.19) and **Vampire** are similar to Goldstein's poems in the imagery of flowers of pain and blood, the destructive power of love, and woman as vampire. When Goldstein planned a second edition, he dedicated the poems to Munch in 1892 and asked him to provide a cover illustration. Munch sent him a pen

7. Frontispiece for E. Goldstein's **Mandragoras, Psychological Poems,** Copenhagen 1892

8

and ink version of **Melancholy.** It was printed as a frontispiece (ill.7), and its contours and strong black and white contrasts show a new boldness which Munch was to develop further a few years later for his prints.

The poet Vilhelm Krag also asked Munch to provide illustrations for a second edition of his poems. Krag was enthusiastic about several of Munch's paintings and included in his first edition of poems (1892) one called 'Night. Painting by Edvard Munch', which was ostensibly his reaction to the picture **Moonlight. Night in St. Cloud.** For the poems, Munch in 1892 designed a title page showing a girl seen from behind, standing under a tree and looking out to the sea (ill.3). The same figure appears in **The Lonely Ones** of 1891 and in the engraving of the same title (ill.14). It is possible that Krag asked Munch to draw this girl for his title page because he liked the painting.

In spite of Munch's own writing and close association with poets, he was not particular about the titles he gave to his pictures. He said that the last thing he thought about when he painted was the title, and he was apt to change it from time to time. Obstfelder, for one, thought that Munch's pictures should not have titles at all, particularly **The Scream.** From the time of his first exhibitions, critics and poets have however changed or tried to improve on Munch's titles to suit their interpretations of his pictures. An instance of this is the painting **Despair,** which Munch exhibited in the first place as 'Sickly mood at sunset.' (ill.8) In no way is there any justification for translating Munch's adjective 'syk' in the title, as some American critics have done, as 'insane'. The Norwegian simply means unhealthy, ill or sick, as in **The Sick Child.** Munch's contemporaries similarly tried to make his titles harsher than he did. It later irritated Munch that the painting he had called 'Love and Pain' became known as 'Vampire'.

The inspiration for **The Scream** was, according to Munch, a poem by Obstfelder. However he originally made the lithograph of **The Scream** look like an illustration for his own creative writing, by showing a prose poem about a sunset which made him feel a cry through nature. When it was printed beside the lithograph in **La Revue Blanche,** the editor explained that 'the text which comments on the lithograph is one of these small poems which Mr. Munch is in the habit of attaching to his compositions. It therefore forms a document in support of what we were saying about the literary preoccupations of the Norwegian painter.' (ill.9) Vance Thompson, the editor of the New York magazine **M'lle,** in January 1896 reprinted the lithograph and commented, 'I have redrawn from a woodcut in 'La Revue Blanche' this whimsical black and white, which is typical of Edvard Munch only in his whimsical mood. The painter himself has put into words his interpretation of the drawing.' (cat. 103) It is remarkable that probably the first time a picture by Munch was printed in French and American magazines, he should be presented not only as an artist, but as a

8. Despair, 1892, oil on canvas, 92 x 67 cm. Thiel Gallery

writer. And why not, seeing that he filled notebooks and loose scraps of paper with his written impressions and ideas? His association with Goldstein, Krag and Obstfelder, who asked him to design vignettes for their poems, can only have increased his interest in writing, adapting and condensing his own texts. While Munch's picture **The Scream** and his text are now often presented as documentary evidence about his life, his contemporaries were justified in seeing in them the product of a poetic imagination.

M. Edvard Munch. Le texte qui la commente est un de ces petits poèmes que M. Munch a l'habitude de joindre à ses compositions. Il constitue donc un document à l'appui de ce que nous disions des préoccupations littéraires du peintre norvégien.

Pour satisfaire à la curiosité manifestée par quelques lecteurs des articles de M. K. V. Hammer et de M. Thadée Natanson sur M. Gunnar Heiberg et sur M. Edvard Munch (La revue blanche du 15 novembre. — CORRESPONDANCE DE KRISTIANIA), nous donnons, ci après, le portrait de M. Gunnar Heiberg par

M. Christian Krogh et la reproduction d'une lithographie de

M'arrêtant, je m'appuyai à la balustrade, presque mort de fatigue. Au-dessus du fjord bleu noir pendaient des nuages, rouges comme du sang et comme des langues de feu. Mes amis s'éloignaient, et, seul, tremblant d'angoisse, je pris conscience du grand cri infini de la nature. — E. M.

9. La Revue Blanche, December 1895

MUNCH'S CHALLENGE TO THE ASSOCIATION OF BERLIN ARTISTS

When Munch had for many years associated with Scandinavian writers and painters who were rebels, he caused a major disruption in the German art world. He was invited to show his paintings under the auspices of the Association of Berlin Artists, in a centre which was in no way prepared for modern art. Munch brought to Berlin 55 canvases which included street scenes from Paris and Oslo, landscapes, pictures of death, portraits and figure studies. When he had hung his pictures, the Germans in the Association were horrified by what they saw. They found Munch's technique a disgrace to art and did not believe that he could be a serious painter. Kaiser Wilhelm II, who tried to influence the Association's taste in art, wanted paintings to be morally uplifting, and only one gallery was bold enough to show French impressionist and neo-impressionist art. The majority in the Association decided to close Munch's exhibition after only four days, but about 88 members protested against the decision by walking out of the meeting and forming their own 'Free Association of Berlin Artists'. They wanted to remain within the official Association but to protect invited guests and to arrange exhibitions of foreign art in Berlin. Their protest was reported in the press as a 'Secession', but the **Berliner Secession** was not a separate body until 1898.

In spite of the overwhelming opposition from the more traditional German painters and critics, Munch had a small group of friends and admirers, many of whom were writers. The German interest in Scandinavian literature was at its zenith, and both the painter Walter Leistikow and the poet Max Dauthendey wrote that Munch had something new to offer in art. Leistikow wrote on 'The Munch Affair' in the **Freie Bühne** in 1892, that 'he who can tell, paint, sing such things, has a poet's disposition, who looks at the world, which he loves, with a poet's eyes. But great poets and painters are seldom understood at first, seldom honoured. They can be glad if they are not shown the door and politely thrown out, like Mr. Munch.'

Apart from his new German friends, Munch enjoyed the company of the Scandinavian colony in Berlin. His former teacher Christian Krohg was there and, as usual, encouraged Munch to be assertive. It appears that it was Krohg and his friends who persuaded Munch to provoke the Association by applying for membership. Krohg wrote in a letter on 8 April 1893, 'we have been causing some trouble in the Artists' Association here, in that we have made Munch apply to join. The Artists' Association is once more divided into two camps. It will be decided on Tuesday. He does not stand an earthly chance of being admitted. But they are in an awful dilemma, and it is fun.' (OUB Brevs. 212) Munch's application was refused by a vote of 77 to 39.

Munch was a threat to the more traditional artists in 1893 because there were liberal critics who wrote in his favour. One wrote that the Association betrayed its prejudice against modern art in refusing Munch's application, because he had quite enough talent to be admitted: 'they ostracised not the bad painter but the modern painter.'[5] Munch himself rose to the challenge and helped to arrange an exhibition of the 'Free Association of Berlin Artists' in June 1893. It consisted of many of the items which had been refused by the jury of

10. **Night in St. Cloud. Moonlight**, 1893, pastel, 80 x 75 cm. Private Collection

the Berlin Academy for its official exhibition. Munch sent his pastels **Interior by Lamplight** and **Night** (ill.10). When Jaro Springer reviewed the exhibition in the July issue of **Die Kunst für Alle**, he rebuked the jury of the Academy for refusing Munch's pastel **Night**, which he described as 'a quite respectable, sensitive study of light'.

Another painter who was far too modern for the taste of the Academy was the bold and inventive Swedish writer August Strindberg. Strindberg painted seascapes and a few almost abstract landscapes. He was a keen photographer, but he painted his seascapes at home in his own room, preferring sunset or moonlight to daylight. He worked almost exclusively with a palette knife to obtain a thick surface of paint, whereas Munch worked from pencil sketches and obtained a more fluid surface by alternating patches of thick paint with paint mixed with turpentine. Strindberg however resembled Munch in that he explored several variations of the same image. He exhibited two of his paintings of the sea shore in Berlin in June 1893, and received rather worse criticism than Munch. One reviewer wrote that their pictures were 'unbelievable filth, which have even started a 'school' as we can see from a few other canvases which are painted green, red and yellow.'[6]

The impact Munch made on other painters was also reported by the Danish writer and former painter Holger Drachmann. He wrote about Munch, 'undoubtedly he has been an explosion here – the anarchist among painters – and he has certainly formed a school: you see that at the exhibition of the young painters.' (cat. 17) But Drachmann added that Munch continued to fight alone, because the younger painters had partly dropped off, fearing the same consequences.

While it is difficult to prove that Munch started a 'school' of painters as early as 1893, there is ample evidence that he attracted the modern writers in Berlin. One of them was Max Dauthendey, who also painted, sketched in pastels and did embroidery. He spent hours in Munch's exhibition in December 1892 and wrote a poem in response to the painting **Vision**. (cat. 92) Dauthendey made much of the colours in Munch's painting, which he interpreted as a vivid and objective juxtaposition of life and death. He also applied his monist ideas to Munch's paintings in his book on the aesthetics of 'intimate' art.[7] Dauthendey found Munch a pioneer in choosing simple motifs with which to explore the gradations of mood with vibrations of light and colour.

Dauthendey was one of the first Germans to write in positive terms about Munch, and he did not hide his identity in a pseudonym, as some of Munch's supporters did. Munch, in turn, was impressed by Dauthendey's writing. In 1898 he wrote of Dauthendey's surrealist booklet on suffering **The Black Sun**, 'many of the moods are remarkably similar to my dreams – and death pictures – and I understand it very well.'[8] His appreciation of poetry and good relations with writers therefore extended to Germans as well as to Scandinavians.

11. **Max Dauthendey**, lithograph 1924, OKK G/I 441

THE ART CRITIC MEIER-GRAEFE ENCOURAGES MUNCH'S EARLY PRINTS

Munch stayed on in Berlin and made friends with many writers and artists who contributed to the most enterprising magazines and journals. In 1894 he began to make prints. People have often wondered why and how he came to try his hand at prints, which were to become a vital aspect of his art. The clue to this may lie in his friendship with Julius Meier-Graefe.

Meier-Graefe was a young engineering student who was persuaded by the Polish writer Przybyszewski to contribute an essay to the first book on Munch's art in 1894. This essay was Meier-Graefe's first attempt at art criticism. From wanting to become a writer, he now devoted himself to art, and actually became one of Germany's most seminal art historians. He was younger than Munch, but sometimes acted as his agent in the 1890s.

In 1894 Meier-Graefe had helped to found **Pan**, a quarterly magazine which was another attempt by the progessive faction in Berlin to expand the knowledge of modern and international art and literature. For the first two issues, Meier-Graefe was the editor for art, Otto Julius Bierbaum for literature; on the board of directors were some of the professors who had defended Munch in the Association of Berlin Artists. Meier-Graefe travelled to Paris, Brussels and London to buy original prints for **Pan**, and Bierbaum visited paper mills and selected different coloured hand-made paper for the magazine. The hub of activity and excitement in planning a new magazine which was to publish the literature and pictures of Munch's friends must have been stimulating to him, who had dreamt of producing a journal with Goldstein a few years earlier.

Some of the artists and organizers of the **Pan** project helped Munch to learn engraving and lithography, and his fine draughtsmanship soon enabled him to master the techniques. Eberhard von Bodenhausen wrote to Munch on 12 December 1894, 'frankly it seems to me as if engraving is your real domain.' (OKK MS) Berlin may not have welcomed foreign painting styles, but it was an excellent centre for printing. In 1895 Munch learnt to make prints by transferring drawings from paper instead of from drawings directly on a stone. However he created his most powerful lithographs by using lithographic ink on stone, for example **The Scream** and **Self-portrait with a skeleton arm**, both of which he printed in Berlin (cat. 15, 4).

For his prints Munch mostly adapted and simplified images which he had created earlier in his drawings, oils and pastels. However he

*Q*UAND *il est sorti   Mais quand il rentra*
(J'entendis la porte)   (J'entendis la lampe)
Quand il est sorti   Mais quand il rentra
Elle avait souri . . .   Une autre était là . .

Et j'ai vu la mort
(J'entendis son âme)
Et j'ai vu la mort
Qui l'attend encore . . .

12. Book design in **Pan**, i, 1895

did not always copy his earlier designs, because they would be reversed by the printing process and so alter the finished composition. He visualized in reverse the image he wanted, and prints like **Jaeger, The Scream, Madonna, Death in the Sick Room** and **The Kiss** resemble the first design in the paintings of the same subject. His technical skill, deliberate design and sensitivity seemed more obvious in his prints than in his paintings.

Letters from Meier-Graefe and Harry Count Kessler indicate that they wanted to help Munch sell pictures through the magazine **Pan**, but according to Meier-Graefe, the extravagance of the magazine was not to Munch's taste.[9] However, Munch's portrait of the Norwegian writer Knut Hamsun was printed as a heliograph in the first issue of **Pan** in 1896 (cat. 27). Hamsun was one of the best of the psychological writers of Munch's generation and after his novel **Pan** was published in 1894, his portrait by Munch was naturally appropriate in the magazine. The choice of the name, **Pan**, for the new venture is even said to have been inspired by Hamsun's novel.

The other artists represented in the magazine reflected the interest in print-making as a form of art, not just as a means of reproducing pictures. In the volumes of **Pan**, Munch could see prints ranging from Dürer and Cranach to Böcklin, Rodin, Käthe Kollwitz, Valloton, Beardsley and van de Velde. By using heliographs and new techniques of colour reproduction on strong etching paper, the prints looked very fine and must have stimulated Munch. He would also notice that the choice of typography, vignettes and decorative borders showed imaginative book design. (ill.12)

Meier-Graefe arranged for the French and German offices of the magazine to sell original graphic work, posters and print portfolios, and Munch's prints were among those advertised for sale in the French supplement to the second issue of 1895. The prints in question were probably 8 of Munch's engravings which Meier-Graefe had produced in a portfolio in June 1895. This was the first of Munch's print portfolios and included some of his earliest small and delicate drypoint engravings (cat. 1, 11, 29-34). The titles given are set below with the present titles in brackets:

> Morning Mood (The Day After)
> Portrait (of Dr. Max Asch)
> The Lonely Ones
> Tête-à-tête
> Moonlight (Night in Saint Cloud)
> Bohême Scene (Christiania Bohême I)
> The Girl at the Window
> The Invalid (The Sick Child)

The introductory essay Meier-Graefe wrote to this portfolio was his

13. **The Sick Child**, 1894, engraving OKK G/r 7

second piece of art criticism, again on Munch. He described Munch as a genius, whose art was a protest against the conventions of his age. He thought that the prints, even if they occasionally appeared a little thin in comparison with the paintings, could be more acceptable to the public; and he observed that this portfolio was representative of Munch's observation of the world around him, not of his fantasy. He vouched for the good likeness of the portrait of Munch's friend the gynaecologist Max Asch, and pointed out that this, as well as **Christiania Bohême I** and **Tête-à-tête** indicated Munch's sense of humour.

Meier-Graefe's introduction to the portfolio is now virtually unknown and very scarce, but must have been encouraging to Munch in 1895. According to Meier-Graefe, the whole point of **The Sick Child** engraving was to draw the girl's delicate, suffering profile, and the older woman was only there as a dark area of contrast. The girl's face was brilliant, in his opinion, and met the real test of the artist, which was simplicity. A year later in 1896, Munch in his lithograph **The Sick Child** omitted the older woman and furnishings, drawing only the girl's face in profile, and it may have been Meier-Graefe's remarks which spurred him to seek even greater simplicity.

The Sick Child engraving differed from the original painting in that Munch removed the window and added below a section of landscape

(ill.13). In other paintings of about 1893, Munch also juxtaposed human transience indoors with the light and growth of nature outside. Otto Julius Bierbaum was moved by the engraving to write a poem 'The Invalid' in which he expressed the innocence and resignation he found in the picture (cat. 28).

Munch's economy of expression often attracted the admiration of his literary friends. Meier-Graefe wrote about the print **The Lonely Ones** (ill.14): 'it is impossible to present more simply the relationship, or rather the absence of a relationship, between the individual and the universe; and I would imagine that Munch, before getting the matter on paper in such a pregnant form, needed several whole days.' Munch did in fact work for years with different drafts and techniques to find expressive designs for his major pictures. But this process is a sign not of an obsessive preoccupation with emotional subject-matter, but of his skill and seriousness as a technician as well as of his artistry.

14. **The Lonely Ones**, 1895, engraving OKK G/r 19

15

MUNCH CREATES A SERIES ON 'LOVE'

The naturalist literature which presented man as biologically determined by his inheritance affected a pessimistic frieze of paintings which Munch exhibited beween 1893 and 1895 as a series called 'Love'. At first, in 1892, he exhibited paintings which refer to memories of his mother and sister's deaths of tuberculosis together with beautiful pictures of the women who loved him or who were his models. In this way he showed images deriving from both his past and his present. He went on to develop images which expressed his bitterness not so much about the convention of marriage as about the trials and loss of his loved ones at home, for whom he found no substitute. Munch was deeply attached to a few women, but remained a bachelor for many reasons, ranging from love of independence to his feeling of financial responsibility in the first place to his aunt and two remaining sisters after his father's death in 1889. His affection for children and association of sexuality with regeneration is evident in many of his pictures. That he should have wanted to scrutinize and express his feelings in a series was largely in response to the literary environment in which he moved. Hans Jaeger had given a precedent in writing about love as a protest against a grim determinism. In the 1890s, Munch met writers who had a greater medical knowledge about psychology and who aimed to compete with doctors in the analysis of emotions. They produced literary case histories of mental disorders and strengthened Munch's interest in psychology and biological determinism. By encouraging a naturalist probing not only into physical phenomena but also into the psyche, they acted as the catalyst for Munch's series on 'love'.

Munch adapted many of the images from his series into prints and exhibited them together with new prints on the theme of mutation in love and death in 1897. However he showed his series together with other of his pictures, such as portraits, landscapes and various prints and drawings, so it was not the only impression he wanted to give of his artistic production. What was significant about the 'Love' series was that it was a daring exposure of subconscious emotion. Munch first confronted people with violent pictures of love and anxiety in Berlin, where he had caused an uproar in the Artists' Association, and where he was described as being 'the anarchist among painters'. (cat. 17) And who were the new friends who encouraged him to expose emotions? They were Nietzsche admirers and Scandinavian writers like the Swedes, Strindberg and Ola Hansson, who had settled in Berlin in the hope of finding a market for books they could not sell at home. They admired Jaeger's novel **From the Christiania Bohême**,

and were themselves concerned to prove the overwhelming power of instinctive spheres of perception. Although they were unaware of Freud's investigations, they had read some of the same medical textbooks. It was after Munch was well established among the intellectuals in Berlin that he in December 1893 exhibited his first 'Love' series. It consisted of **The Voice, The Kiss, Vampire, Madonna, Melancholy** and **The Scream.**

When Munch was rejected by the Association of Berlin Artists, he was welcomed by a more imaginative and international group of writers, artists, students and doctors who met in a tavern called 'At the Black Piglet'. Munch wrote home on 20 January 1893 that he was constantly together with the writers Strindberg, Heiberg, Drachmann and Adolf Paul and that they met in a small wine tavern. Apart from their enjoyment of art, music, dance, poetry and the theatre, it was an intense interest in psychology which united the central members of the group. Several of them were stimulated by 'psycho-physiology', and such research encouraged artists and writers to express a subjective experience of reality. Moreover Hansson, Strindberg and Przybyszewski were familiar with the books on the power of suggestion by the French doctors Bernheim and Liégeois in 1884 and on the failure of will power discussed by Ribot in 1885. Munch could see in Berlin plays by Strindberg which demonstrated medical theories about fluctuations in the mind and heart. When he wrote about Strindberg in about 1912, he described his impression of the first performances of Strindberg's plays. They were **The Creditors, The First Warning** and **Before Death**, on 22 January 1893, and **Playing with Fire** in December 1893. Munch is certain to have been in the audience of at least the first three one-act experimental plays.

Strindberg tried to accelerate the exposure of inner life and make it more obvious than in Ibsen's plays, so he exaggerated the mental tension, using distortion of character, time and place. His characters are jealous and neurotic, haunted by their past memories of love and intimacy, as of skeletons in a cupboard or under the floorboards. Strindberg's book **The Red Room** had been an inspiration to Hans Jaeger in his **From the Christiania Bohême**, and his novels and plays expressing the power of heredity, environment, memories, guilt, jealousy and inner anxiety gave an impetus to Munch's pictures like **Ashes** and **Jealousy**. (ill.15).

The model for the foreground figure in Munch's **Jealousy** was Paul Hermann, an artist of satirical drawings and etchings. The liaison in the background suggests that he is obsessed by something he has seen or imagined, but there is no evidence that Hermann had flashes of jealousy, any more than that the 11 year old girl who was the model for **The Sick Child** was herself ill. Munch used faces to express a particular situation in much the same way that Strindberg and Przybyszewski exaggerated or changed characters to make vivid a psychological scene.

Munch in Berlin in 1893-4 created versions of **The Girl and Death,
Madonna, Vampire, Separation, Puberty** and **Rose and Amelie**, as
well as portraits of friends. His paintings show more explicitly erotic
images than before and a greater concentration on the psychology of
women. **Rose and Amelie** was exhibited as 'Interior' in December
1893 and gives a less sympathetic view of prostitutes than the one
advanced by Jaeger and Krohg in the 1880s. Munch's friends
meanwhile watched the development of his pictures with interest.
Adolf Paul remembered seeing him paint **Puberty**, and he himself

15. **Jealousy II**, 1896, lithograph OKK G/I 202

knelt for the man in the painting **Vampire**. Meier-Graefe wrote to Munch in July 1894 that he hoped to acquire a version of **Separation** which he called 'The Hair Picture' and which he thought would be Munch's masterpiece if he painted it with care.

What were Munch's literary associates producing in 1893? Strindberg asked Adolf Paul to take one of his French manuscripts of 'Le Plaidoyer d'un Fou' to a publisher in Berlin, and it was printed anonymously in German in May. Of the various English translations of the book, the one which is based on the original French is called **A Madman's Manifesto** (cat. 61). It must have been this book that weighed on Strindberg's conscience when he expressed his disgust in **The Cloister** (1898) that one of the things a writer could do was to use his wife as an experimental rabbit. **A Madman's Manifesto** opens with the narrator's vision of a struggle with death and continues with his version of the process by which his wife drives him mad. In 1893 Przybyszewski published **Requiem Mass**, in which the experience of love caused the death of a hypersensitive individual. These books appear to have influenced Munch in his choice of imagery in 1893, and indeed he once said that his drawing **The Girl and Death** had been intended for the frontispiece to a book which he, Przybyszewski and Strindberg had planned to publish jointly.[10] (ill.16).

Tracing the development of Munch's iconography, it appears that 1893 was the year in which he intensified the expression of simultaneous physical and psychical levels of perception. Perhaps he was following the example of Strindberg and Przybyszewski in exposing a cross-section of different sensations. Munch's version of **Despair** in 1892 lets a figure peer over the jetty railing into the water below (ill.8). In 1893 the same figure is no longer in profile but faces the spectator, ears clutched, mouth open, to project forward the mood of alarm. Munch's versions of **The Kiss** in 1890-2 showed a couple, dressed, in a room with a window. **The Girl and Death** of 1893 shows a girl, naked, embracing a skeleton, with no clear background but sperm cells and embryos closing in on them (cat. 53). The painting **Madonna** of 1893 was originally in a similar setting.

It was while Munch associated with literary friends that his love and death images appeared in profusion. Using the coastline of Aasgaardstrand as a common background, he gradually built up his series. In **Attraction** he simply placed a couple of heads in front of a soft, evocative landscape which he had painted in 1893 (cat. 49). In **Separation** he added a girl to the sinuous coastline and gloomy profile of the man he had drawn in **Melancholy**.

Sometimes Munch wrote texts to accompany his pictures. He may have intended to publish them because the one he wrote in German for **Separation** was corrected by a friend. In the group 'At the Black Piglet' he acquired the reputation of being very perceptive about literature and of being a writer of some distinction. One of his

16. **The Girl and Death**, 1894, engraving OKK G/r 3

acquaintances wrote that during their gatherings in the tavern, Munch used to write on scraps of paper, that he turned his brilliant ideas into words.[11] When the German writer Peter Hille planned a review for literature, art and music in about 1893, he wrote that he would welcome aphorisms from Munch.[12]

Munch was receptive to his literary environment in Berlin, where he read poems by Obstfelder, and was invited out by German critics,

publishers and the actress who was the leading lady in Strindberg's **The Creditors** in January 1893. Jens Thiis remembers that in Berlin he and Munch also read Gunnar Heiberg's play **The Balcony** 'with great emotion'. (OUB MS). Munch found a parallel between this play and his painting **Sphinx. The Woman in Three Stages**, because when he first exhibited the picture in 1894, he quoted a line from the play in his catalogue: '62. Sphinx. 'All the others are one. You are a thousand.'

17. Sphinx. The Woman in Three Stages, 1894, oil on canvas, 164 x 250 cm., Rasmus Meyer's Collection, Bergen

Studier till en stämningsserie: "Kärlek".

55. Sommarnattsmystik.
56. Man och kvinna.
57. I skogen.
58. \
59. / Kyss.
60. \
61. / Kvinnan som älskar.
62. Sfinx.

   »Alle de andre er en. Du er tusen». (Gunnar Heiberg: Balkonen.)

63. \
64. / Vampyr.
65. Händer.
66. Svartsjuka.
67. Sjuk stämning.
68. Skrik.
69. Vignett.

———

70. Diverse teckningar.

Stockholm, Iduns Tryckeri Aktiebolag, 1894.

18. Catalogue to Munch's exhibition in the Stockholm Art Association's premises, 1894

(Gunnar Heiberg: The Balcony.)' (ill.18) The central woman in Munch's painting compares with Heiberg's main character Julie, a woman with long dark hair, whose lover calls to her in her bedroom, 'no, remain standing like that. With your arm raised up high. Stay standing. Everything in you is new. Yes, smile! All the others are one. You are a thousand.' (cat. 26) The leading male role is of a reflective type of man whom both Munch and Heiberg portrayed as brooding on the deceptive and changeable nature of love. Munch presented the situation in **The Woman in Three Stages**, where a man turns away from the women.

From 1893 onwards, while he lived in Germany, Norway and Paris, Munch's 'Love' series developed into his most pessimistic investigation into creativity. It included the pictures for which he is best known and which reflect the interest in psychology which he shared with his literary and medical friends. In it he expressed the subconscious depths of what he had seen, felt and imagined both in himself and in others. It was his main response in art to his literary associates.

19. **Separation I**, 1896, lithograph OKK G/l 209

PRZYBYSZEWSKI URGES THE ABANDONMENT OF CONSCIOUSNESS

20. Stanislaw Przybyszewski, 1898, lithograph OKK G/l 231

Throughout his life Munch made friends with doctors and with people who had an expert knowledge of medicine. One of those who was particularly important for the development of his pictures in the 1890s was Stanislaw Przybyszewski. Przybyszewski was a medical student from June 1890 to July 1893. He took a special interest in neurology and was awarded a Polish scholarship on the strength of his study of the spinal cord structure. The detailed diagrams of ganglions which he drew in his course book were so good that they helped the doctor Carl Schleich in his discovery of local anaesthesia. Schleich and his friends called Przybyszewski 'the gory physiologist'. As a writer Przybyszewski wanted to explore regions below conscious ratiocination and he aimed to show the cerebral layers of the self being torn to shreds. Many of his narratives are concerned with the exposure of neurosis, and virtually all his stories project moods of anxiety and suffering. He was evidently important to Munch's art because Munch once said that he and Przybyszewski had discussed artistic and psychical ways of influencing each other.[13]

Przybyszewski was keenly interested in the contemporary psychological investigation into the way rhythms or thought waves could pass from one mind to another through the power of suggestion or hypnotism. He extended this to the conviction that rhythms or vibrations could be interchanged between music, literature and painting. When Munch wrote about Przybyszewski in 1928, he expressed his admiration for his friend's mesmeric hold over his audience when he had played the piano:

> he could suddenly leap up in ecstasy and rush to the piano in such haste as if following inner voices which called him. And during the deathly silence which followed, the immortal music of Chopin resounded through the narrow room and transformed it suddenly into a radiant festival hall, a shrine of art. And he was so completely carried away and he interpreted the wonderful paintings of his great compatriot with such mastery, that he made us listen, breathless, fascinated, oblivious of time and place, until the last chord died away. (cat. 38)

Munch therefore approved of the mixing of the arts, as his reference to Chopin's 'wonderful paintings' shows. Przybyszewski was rhythmic but deliberately uncontrolled and technically inaccurate when he played the piano because he thought that this method conveyed passion. The dripmarks, shadows and violation of form in Munch's Berlin paintings suggest a similar degree of intensity.

When Przybyszewski tried to describe the vibrations in a person's mind in his writing, he would abstract certain expressive features of the stimulant, and exaggerate them. He often made his characters unable to distinguish between dreams and reality. So in **De Profundis** (1895), a man 'tried hard to see clearly and distinguish from each other the people who glided past him like shadows.' In his narratives

Przybyszewski virtually denied the external world and reduced plot to a sequence of moods and random workings of the mind, often with vivid colours and repetition to give the impression of fluidity. In his story 'Ascenscion', printed in the **Moderner Musenalmanach** in 1894, he wrote, 'all his thoughts circled round in confusion. They described wide elliptical lines. They stretched out. They whirled and glowed and darted around.' The strange, fluctuating effect can be compared with Munch's pictures like **Anxiety, The Scream** and **Fever/By the Deathbed** (cat. 36, 100, 106).

Przybyszewski often made cross-references to Munch's paintings when he wanted to suggest certain sensations of pain or pleasure in his narratives. He even wrote a novel about a painter who had wanted to paint a scream he had heard from a woman who threw herself over the railings of a bridge into the water below. Munch, in turn, portrayed

21. **Virginia Creeper**, 1900, oil on canvas, 119.5 x 121 cm. Munch Museum

Przybyszewski several times and it looks as if he also adapted Przybyszewski's bearded face for a male prototype when he wanted to show a man's face suffering emotional disturbance. In **Virginia Creeper**, such a figure is placed in front of the building which used to be the liquor store in Aasgaardstrand (ill.21).

Under the influence of Przybyszewski, Munch's pictures became more wild and hallucinatory, and the poet Richard Dehmel was reproached in 1896 for having succumbed to a 'munch-pzbschwkisch narcosis,' presumably in his poems **Woman and World**.[14] Przybyszewski certainly encouraged Munch to probe into psychical and daemonic areas of perception, and Munch used his insight to project a sense of dissolution and the intuitive awareness of death. Munch's interest in the occult appears to have been directed towards spiritualism and telepathy. Several of the Berlin group attended spiritualist sessions and contributed to the occultists' journal **Sphinx** which Przybyszewski edited in 1897 when it was renamed **Metaphysische Rundschau**. Przybyszewski in his memoirs wrote that Munch had enjoyed reading **Spiritismus und Animismus** by the Russian spiritualist Aksakow and Swedenborg's **De Coelo et Inferno**. One of the surprising habits of Munch's father had been to tell his children very vivid ghost stories, and a friend remarked that Munch in later life was not afraid of ghosts.[15]

In the mid-1890s Munch created a psychical dimension in his paintings and prints by mysterious, waving lines around subjects like **Madonna** and **The Scream**, lines giving the impression that the subject is insubstantial, and which might suggest an aura such as those Swedenborg believed he saw around people. Moreover some of Munch's women have large, dark eyes, for example in **The Voice**. (cat. 40) It was in part the preoccupation with theories on mesmerism and spiritualism in the 1880s and 1890s that made Munch, Hansson, Strindberg and Przybyszewski show love as such a destructive force, turning the weaker person into a mirror of the stronger, or haunted by subconscious guilt and past memories.

That Munch's presentation of the intermingling of life and death had a lasting and compelling power was due to his ability as an artist. His evocation of the past and the future on the present was not vague but was often based on his present, vivid arrangement of his models. In the pastel and lithograph **Death in the Sick Room** (cat. 63), he showed his brothers and sisters in a group as they looked when they were adults, but the situation with the invalid in the chair refers to the death of his oldest sister in 1877 when she was 15. Munch here reads into the brothers' and sisters' faces and gestures the memory of a scene they had witnessed 16 years earlier, when they were aged between 9 and 13. As in a play by Ibsen, or a short story by Ola Hansson, the figures are haunted by what they remember.

Przybyszewski published an enthusiastic review, called 'Psychic

Naturalism', of Munch's paintings (cat. 55), and he persuaded Franz Servaes, Willy Pastor and Julius Meier-Graefe to contribute essays to a book on Munch which appeared in July 1894. Through his analysis of subconscious emotions, Przybyszewski had been the main influence on Munch's paintings of love and death in 1893-4. He was the first to organize publicity for the pictures and he was emphatic about Munch's significance for the development of modern art. In his book **On the Paths of the Soul** (1897), he praised Munch and Vigeland for exposing instinctive reactions to love, violence and suffering (cat. 56). He described them as 'northern psychologists of sexuality' whose art represented an alternative to the external naturalism of a painter like Liebermann and to the contemporary refined and chaste art of

anaemic maidens and pale youths which was too weak to cope with pain or 'the death rattle and triumphant scream of life.' It seems appropriate that Munch placed bones beneath Przybyszewski's face in one of his portraits of him in 1894-5. This friend had given him the strongest stimulus to express subterranean and macabre levels of awareness.

After Munch's association with Strindberg and Przybyszewski in the winter of 1892-3, the tragic aspect of his work became more dominant. Death was not only a corpse laid out or a skeleton; he showed it as a presence in life for those who were not among the fittest and best equipped for survival. Munch in the 1890s hardly portrayed supermen, but those who were failures, and he did this with a unique power.

NIETZSCHE: A VISION OF CONTRADICTIONS

The emphasis on pain and conflict in the literature of Munch's friends owed much to Friedrich Nietzsche. Nietzsche's exposure of antagonism in the mind, his attack on Christian ideals and his insistence on subjectivity had a radical impact on Scandinavian and German aesthetics from 1888 onwards. One of the reasons why he was welcomed by the generation of the Symbolists was that he was not furtive about subconscious powers in human nature but encouraged a frank attitude to the Dionysiac. The enthusiasm for Nietzsche's ideas was apparent in some interpretations of Munch's art, and as early as 1893 Munch himself expressed his admiration for Nietzsche in a letter to Rohde.

Nietzsche had corresponded with Strindberg for six weeks in the winter of 1888-9, immediately before his mental collapse. He had encouraged Strindberg's misogyny, writing about the play **The Father**, 'I read your tragedy twice and was deeply moved; I was extremely surprised to find a work in which my concept of love – in its means of war, in its basis of deathly hatred between the sexes – was expressed in a splendid way.'[16]

It soon became obvious to Strindberg and his friends that Nietzsche, the literary lion, had been reduced to a physical and mental wreck. As Harold Borland has pointed out, it is likely that memories of the megalomania and final madness in Nietzsche's letters may have prompted Strindberg to describe the mental collapse of the character Borg at the end of the novel **By the outer Skerries** in

1890.[17] Strindberg talked about his letters from Nietzsche to Karl Strecker and other friends when he was in the tavern 'At the Black Piglet'.

The knowledge that Nietzsche was ill affected the interpretation of his work by Munch's friends, and gave rise to numerous depictions of self-destruction and of madness and genius. Przybyszewski turned from a study of architecture to neurology after reading Nietzsche, and his writing on art showed his receptivity to Nietzsche's idea of the Dionysiac. Przybyszewski went to Weimar in the winter of 1892-3, when he was in close contact with Munch, and saw Nietzsche in a wheelchair on his verandah, helpless, apparently bereft of speech and sight. Przybyszewski remembered this as one of the most tragic impressions of his life. In his book **Concerning the Psychology of the Individual** (1892), he treated Nietzsche as a case history of an over-cerebral man.

Munch never saw or met Nietzsche, but he knew his sister and drew posthumous portraits of the philosopher with the help of photographs (ill.22). It is not clear which of Nietzsche's works other than **Thus spake Zarathustra** were known to him, but he wrote to Ernest Thiel, who commissioned the Nietzsche portrait, 'I have portrayed him as the writer of Zarathustra in his cave between the mountains. – He stands on his verandah and looks down into a deep valley. A radiant sun is rising over the mountains. It could allude to the passage where he speaks about standing in the light but wishing he were in the dark – but also to some of his other works.'[18] The passage he alluded to was probably Zarathustra's 'Night Song'. Delius had set it to music in 1898 and may well have discussed it with Munch when Munch stayed with him a few months before the song was first performed in 1903. In 1905 Delius incorporated it into **A Mass of Life**.

22. **Friedrich Nietzsche**, 1906, lithograph OKK G/l 263

Munch's paintings of **The Sun** and related murals for the University of Oslo Festival Hall in 1910-16 have sometimes been compared with Nietzsche's **Zarathustra**. However the chief male figure in the murals was not based on a lonely prophet in the high mountains 'wishing he were in the dark,' but on an old fisherman who talks to a child. The people who figure predominantly in Munch's art at that time were workers. After a prolonged absence, Munch was moreover discovering with renewed pleasure the beauty of Norway and her coast, where he chose to settle in 1909.

The lithograph of Nietzsche is based on the head section of the portraits and sketches of 1905-6, and omits the diagonal verandah wall and the valley in the background, which are similar in composition to **The Scream**. When the portrait was exhibited in Stockholm shortly after the First World War, Munch said, 'I have painted in him the man who saw the whole war approaching, he who brutally and staunchly looked quite mercilessly into the future.'[19]

MUNCH IN PARIS, 1896-7

Whereas Munch had rocked the Berlin Art Association, he was little known in Paris and he held relatively few exhibitions there. He would have liked to establish a reputation in France and frequently sent a few paintings to the **Salon des Indépendants**, but it was chiefly Germany which became his second home, and where he found patrons and publicity. The most significant aspect of his visit to Paris from February 1896 until the spring of 1897 was that he expanded his graphic production. In 1895 Munch had changed his engraving and combined it with different techniques of printing. During his time in Paris, his graphic designs became freer and he experimented with different processes. He learnt the technique of colour lithography from the printer Auguste Clot, in whose workshop he had the opportunity of seeing prints by Toulouse-Lautrec and other French master print-makers. Clot printed Munch's colour lithographs from several stones. Munch also produced coloured etchings and he coloured black and white lithographs by hand, or printed on tinted papers. In 1896 he began to do woodcuts, in which he excelled and which he at times printed himself by hand. For the colour woodcuts he sometimes sawed up different sections of the woodblock, inked them separately, then re-assembled them for printing. He would also use another woodblock or linocut to produce additional details of line, colour or texture. To let the woodgrain show on the finished print was an effective background for a print like **The Kiss** (cat. 41). Munch also combined different graphic techniques for the same print, mixing woodcuts and lithographs, as in **Vampire** (cat. 42), and in all, he showed a zest for experiment and a subtle use of colour.

After the Meier-Graefe portfolio, Munch in 1896-7 transferred some of his paintings of love and death into prints for a series he planned to publish as 'The Mirror'. He also intended to publish a portfolio with his prints of contemporary writers, which may have spurred him to do his portraits of Mallarmé and Strindberg. The lithograph of Mallarmé was printed off the same block as the Strindberg lithograph, six weeks later (cat. 48). Although Munch met Mallarmé, he probably used a photograph of the poet as the basis for his portraits in a lithograph and drypoint engraving. In a letter from Fontainebleau, Mallarmé wrote to thank Munch for his portrait, in which he said he recognized his own self.

Munch could read and write in French and he liked Mallarmé's poetry. He was also preoccupied with the poetry of Baudelaire in 1896 because a Monsieur Piat commissioned him to draw illustrations of Baudelaire's **Flowers of Evil** for an edition for the society 'Les cent Bibliophiles.' Munch's previous experience of designing illustrations for poetry and his familiarity with magazines like **Pan** stood him in

LE MORT JOYEUX

23. Sketch for Baudelaire's 'Le Mort Joyeux', (from **The Flowers of Evil**), 1896, OKK T 402

24. Advertisement for Ibsen's Peer Gynt, 1896, lithograph OKK G/l 216

good stead. He worked on the drawings in April and May 1896, but Piat died in May, and the project was terminated. Two of Munch's drawings clearly refer to specific poems, 'Gladly Dead' and 'Carrion', because he drew the titles and left a space for the text (cat. 58). In 'Carrion' the poet states that he will keep the memory of the woman he loves alive in his poetry after she is a rotting corpse. Munch had reflected on the inter-relationship of life and death in art for some years, and Baudelaire was yet another writer who prompted him to illustrate the theme.

Although Munch printed with Clot, and had every opportunity of seeing the work of modern French artists, most of his associates seem to have been literary men rather than painters. It was above all people who enjoyed poetry and the theatre who befriended him. He knew some of the critics and authors who published in the magazines **Le**

Mercure de France, La Revue Blanche and **La Plume**, and he again found himself in the company of symbolist writers who were interested in psychology and the occult.[20]

Ibsen and Strindberg were becoming known in Paris through the performances of their plays and Munch knew some of their translators and producers. He designed theatre advertisements for the French première of Ibsen's **Peer Gynt** and **John Gabriel Borkman** at the Théâtre de l'Oeuvre (cat. 65-6). This theatre had opened with a performance of Ibsen's **Rosmersholm** in 1893 and in the season for 1895-6 it showed not only **Peer Gynt** but also Heiberg's plays **The Balcony** and **The Large Prize**. Together with the plays by Maeterlinck, the Scandinavians contributed to the movement for intimism in the theatre.

MUNCH'S IMPRESSIONS OF STRINDBERG

In Paris Munch met old friends from Norway and Berlin: Obstfelder, Vilhelm Krag, Delius, Meier-Graefe, Dauthendey, Strindberg. The Irish poet Yeats met Strindberg and Dauthendey in Paris and wrote in his **Autobiographies** about Strindberg, 'he and his circle were pre-occupied with the deepest problems of mankind.'[21] Strindberg was busy with pseudo-scientific and botanical studies in Paris, as well as being interested in the occult. Munch drew a lithograph of him there and tried to make Strindberg look forceful because Strindberg had complained that Munch's oil portrait of him in 1892 was not grand enough and that one of Munch's drawings of him in 1893 had shown him with slanted eyes. Strindberg was short and brushed his hair upwards to look taller, hence the great mane of hair over his face in the lithograph (ill.25). The first state of this lithograph was without a frame, the second had a frame of waving lines and a naked woman on the right, and the author's name misspelt 'A. Stindberg'. The element of caricature in the frame may have been Munch's retaliation to Strindberg's satirical and anti-feminist review of his paintings (cat. 44).

Although Munch and Strindberg never met again after 1896, Strindberg's German translator Emil Schering arranged for Strindberg's texts and Munch's pictures to be printed side by side in the **Quickborn** magazine in January 1899 (cat. 60). For the cover Munch designed an image of anguish, **The Flower of Pain**, and for Strindberg's stories **Silverswamp** and **Up to the Sun** he drew some

landscapes. Strindberg was reluctant to appear together with Munch and he disliked the illustrations. However the most lurid of them, **Harpy** and **Kiss of Death**, were a reflection on Strindberg's own sadistic text in his play **Simoom**, in which he had introduced elements of Satanism to bring about a psychical murder. An Arabian girl and her lover terrify a French soldier with macabre suggestions in a sepulchral chamber with a sarcophagus in the middle. She holds a skull in front of the soldier and tells him it is his mirror. It is the context of Strindberg's play which explains the emphasis on destruction in these illustrations. Munch designed clear and bold images which he later converted into separate prints.

Another of Strindberg's projections of mental cruelty with which Munch was familiar was 'A Madman's Manifesto.' (cat. 61). It was the fifth volume of Strindberg's autobiography and was written in French. Strindberg himself admitted that it was a 'terrible book', and was irritated when a Swedish newspaper printed a pirated edition of the German translation in 1893. Nevertheless, he had tried to get it published in Germany or France since 1891. One of his manuscripts lay with a French publisher, and Strindberg gave another to a publisher in Berlin. Munch somehow acquired one of the French manuscripts, apparently the original which Strindberg sold in May 1895 in Paris, after it had been published in French.

The narrator in 'A Madman's Manifesto' repeatedly confesses his feelings of sexual attraction and disillusionment, and describes his wife with deliberate polarity as a madonna or demon. The presentation of the interaction between men and women in some of Munch's paintings between 1898-1908, for example in the **Death of Marat** series, suggest that he, too, wanted to turn his memory of a close

25. **August Strindberg**, 1896, lithograph OKK G/I 219a

relationship with a woman into a dramatic presentation of sexual conflict (cat. 62). Perhaps it was also Strindberg's precedent which led him to compile a ledger called **The Notes of a Madman**. His own bitter feelings about the woman whom he considered the cause of his breakdown in 1908-9 may have made him revise his opinion of Strindberg.[22] In 1896 he had thought Strindberg rather mad when the latter suspected him and his friends of trying to gas him (Brev 186 and cat. 45). In about 1912 Munch wrote in warm terms about Strindberg and his books:

Baccarat [orgies?] in his honour
– and afterwards inclined for friendship with his friends in The Black Piglet
– where he sat with his gigantic joke
– and his little smile now sarcastic now childlike
Then in Paris – where he turned his pain to pearls
– and had to enter the deepest pit of Hell
– strode on almost eagerly
Strindberg looked away – We look away –
Two rows of pictures emerge
– from our daily communion in Berlin
in the winter of 1892-3
At the end of the table in the Black Piglet, surrounded by Germans,Danes, Swedes, Finns, Norwegians and Russians – wildly acclaimed by the young German poets –
Especially Dehmel – who stood up on the table so that the bottles tumbled over – and acclaimed him
And the first performances of his plays –
– Speeches that rang like sword-blows
– shapely words – now like rapiers, now like daggers
– seething like the wine before us
– glowing red, glowing white, dripping,sweating
– burning all around him
– and now rose up bearing in his hands for us Inferno
– and Legends
– Surely the most remarkable novels since Raskolnikow

It began for us Norsemen with The Red Room – that world that is called Strindberg.[23]

This notebook entry is an instance of Munch's sympathetic observation of other people. The evening in 'The Black Piglet' which he, Adolf Paul and other habitués described in their memoirs was the party on 16 January 1893 after the Scandinavian soirée held by the Free Literary Society, which Munch attended. Dehmel, flushed with wine, made speeches, improvised in verse and declaimed the poem 'A Man for Eternity' which he had written in Strindberg's honour. Towards the morning, Dehmel climbed on the table, and swinging his stick around his head, he began to break the bottles on the walls of the narrow tavern room. Strindberg hid under the table. A few days later he celebrated the first performance of three of his one-act plays in Berlin. Munch watched Strindberg in his ups and downs and admired his dramatization of inner conflict.

AUGUST STRINDBERG
EDVARD MUNCH

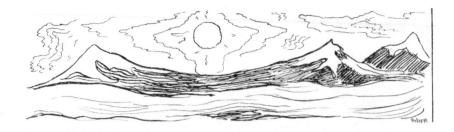

AUF ZUR SONNE.

Die Sonne hat drei lange Wochen in dem kleinen Dorfe Gersau am Vierwaldstättersee nicht geschienen, nicht mehr geschienen seit Anfang Oktober, da der Föhn ging. Nach Sonnenuntergang wurde es ganz windstill und ich schlief die halbe Nacht bis ich von dem Läuten der Kirchenglocke und einem Poltern geweckt wurde, das in des Sturmes eigentümliches Sausen aufgelöst werden konnte wenn er sich über die Alpen

friedvoll dass man nach einem Erdbeben verlangt. Wo die Lichtquelle zu wirken aufhört, lassen alle Farben nach; das Auge wird stumpf und die Seele in eine Schläfrigkeit gehüllt die der Faulheit nahe liegt.

Als ich mich eines Abends vor dem Amtmann über den langen Abschied beklagte den die Sonne genommen, antwortete er mit der Ruhe die einem Deutsch-Schweizer eigen ist:

26. Ibsen in the Grand Café, 1897/1902, lithograph OKK G/L 244

Towering over all Munch's other literary associates was Henrik Ibsen. Ibsen was a contemporary of Munch's father and was 35 years older than Munch, but he was consistently ahead of the younger generation in focussing attention on issues which interested them. Ibsen moreover encouraged the young rebels, Heiberg, Przybyszewski and Munch by telling them that if they caused offence, they were sure to have talent. Ibsen's popularity in the German and French theatres in the 1890s paved the way for other Scandinavians, and Munch to some extent followed his pattern in becoming known first in Germany, and then gradually throughout the western world in his life-time.

New evidence about Munch's contact with Ibsen is an undated letter to the German literary critic Julius Elias. Elias was one of the first Germans to welcome Munch regularly to his home and to buy his pictures. Elias was also a good friend of Ibsen's, and the editor of the first complete edition of his works in German in 1898. Munch wrote to Elias from his family's home in Nordstrand that he was about to go to Paris, that he had talked to Ibsen some time ago and had given him Elias' regards which pleased him. He added that he would probably paint Ibsen's picture soon (cat. 86). Munch gave a full account in later years of how he had made contact with Ibsen through Elias. He wrote that Elias asked him to go and give Ibsen his regards when next in Norway, and that in the spring of 1893 he had duly called at Ibsen's home to deliver Elias' card, but was relieved to find that Ibsen was out. Shortly afterwards, he saw Ibsen reading the foreign newspapers in the Grand Hotel's reading Room in the basement of no. 6 Karl Johan Street:

> There in the corner by the window on to Karl Johan, half in shadows, sits Ibsen behind his newspaper – with his large gleaming eye behind his glasses, he glances around in the room now and again – Here he used to settle every day before dinner – read the newspapers and have a drink – Here he had a little contact with the Europe he had left behind – (cat. 87)

After Munch had read some German newspapers, he left the Reading Room and went into the Café of the Grand Hotel, where Ibsen followed him and headed for his table: 'Good day – are you not Mr. Munch – Thankyou for the visit – and he sat down – He inquired after his friends – we could scarcely talk because of the emotion – Then he left – he had returned the visit.'

Munch met Ibsen from time to time when he was in Norway in the following years. He painted and drew Ibsen's portrait many times, but Ibsen does not appear to have sat for him. The first portrait was drawn in France for the theatre advertisement for **John Gabriel Borkman** in 1897, and it may have been based on Valloton's drawing of Ibsen which was reproduced in **La Revue Blanche** in August 1895 and several other times. Munch also painted and drew portraits of Ibsen by the window in the Grand Hotel in the following years (ill.26). The

27. Manuscript of Munch's reminiscences of Ibsen

background of the curtain and window convey Munch's own memories of the writer sitting reading the newspapers and glancing around the room with his large gleaming eye. Like Strindberg, Ibsen was short, but Munch increased their stature by concentrating on the head and exaggerating their hair and Ibsen's piercing eye.

The fact that German friends like Elias asked Munch to contact Ibsen, may have aroused Ibsen's curiosity about Munch as a painter. Ibsen, who had painted and collected pictures himself, went to Munch's exhibition in Oslo in the autumn of 1895. In **La Revue Blanche**, 15 April 1896, Thadée Natanson reported Ibsen's interest in Munch's exhibition. This proves that Munch was justified in writing later that Ibsen had come up to him, had expressed his interest and had wanted Munch to accompany him around and explain the pictures. The exhibition included the 'Love' series with **Melancholy, Jealousy, Madonna** and **The Scream**. According to Munch in his booklet **The Origin of the Frieze of Life**, Ibsen was particularly arrested by **The Woman in Three Stages**. (ill.7) Munch wrote:

> I had to explain it to him. There is the dreaming woman, the woman greedy for life and the woman as nun – she who stands with a pale face behind the trees. He enjoyed my portraits where I had emphasized the telling features to the extent that they approached caricature. (cat. 88)

Ibsen at the time was working on **John Gabriel Borkman** which has a rich combination of women, and he may well have been impressed by Munch's overlapping and juxtaposed figures, for example in **The Woman in Three Stages** and its variation **Red and White**. (cat. 111). According to Munch, Ibsen confided that this new play 'is going to be something fiendish, this one too ... Yes, yes, people will probably not understand it – They still do not understand Peer Gynt – I meant here – the whole nation.' (cat. 87)

Although Munch was abroad for much of the time between 1891 and 1906, when Ibsen lived in Oslo, they were on friendly terms. In a letter of 17 November 1905, Munch asked if a relation could give his regards to Ibsen and added, 'he really was extremely kind to me.' He wrote that they might have had more contact if they had not both become ill. (Brev 241) Ibsen suffered his first stroke in 1900 and he died in 1906. In the following decades until Munch's own death in 1944, he found in Ibsen's plays his main source of literary material. What did he find in Ibsen more than in any other writer? Dreamers, death scenes, ghosts, loneliness, panic in different guises, individual trials, a double perspective, irony, satire, the power of the past over the present, a piercing perception of women and of daemonic areas of awareness. Munch's illustrations are a reflection on the diversity in Ibsen's plays, ranging from a loneliness in family life in **Ghosts**, to the light-hearted dancing of Anitra in **Peer Gynt** (ill.30). More than that, Munch found it easy to identify with Ibsen's characters, with Osvald,

Rubek and Peer Gynt, and he freely mixed scenes based on his own observations with scenes which illustrate Ibsen's plays.

Ibsen may have seen some of Munch's portraits of him and the theatre advertisement for **Peer Gynt** at the Théâtre de l'Oeuvre in 1896. For the latter, Munch adapted the complementary black and white figures in **The Woman in Three Stages**, which had interested Ibsen, into a composition with two women, Aase and Solveig (ill.23). It is interesting that he did not choose to depict Peer in any of his adventures but the women who love him and wait for him. When the giant Boyg was unable to defeat Peer in his play, the Voice says, 'he was too strong. There were women behind him.' George Bernard Shaw saw the première in Paris and reported that two of the scenes which really moved the audience were when Solveig joined Peer in the mountains and when Aase died.[24] So Munch's drawing anticipated and synthetized two of the most convincing figures in the play. In 1898 Munch did a woodcut of **Women on the Beach** which is a more powerful, simplified variation of the **Peer Gynt** illustration. In the woodcut the counterpoint of a light and dark figure anticipate Irene and her dark keeper in Ibsen's last play **When we dead awaken** of 1899. Munch was firmly convinced that this play showed the influence of his exhibition of 1895 on Ibsen and that the female characters were modelled on his painting **The Woman in Three Stages**. Whether or not this was the case, there are many points of comparison between Ibsen and Munch's presentation of women.

MUNCH'S DESIGNS FOR IBSEN'S GHOSTS

28. Scene design for Ibsen's **Ghosts**, 1906

To mark Ibsen's death in 1906, the German theatre director Max Reinhardt decided to open his new, intimate theatre in Berlin, the 'Kammerspieltheater', with a performance of Ibsen's **Ghosts**. Reinhardt attached great importance to the creation of atmosphere in the theatre and he asked Munch to provide sketches for the décor. In the first instance Munch was asked to provide a drawing with a view through the window onto the landscape outside. Reinhardt wrote very detailed notes of his plan for the interior of **Ghosts**: the Norwegian living room should have dark recesses and corners with strange old-fashioned furniture which could have a sinister effect in the dark. The chair covers and curtains were to be dark, perhaps a worn-out purple. The landscape through the rear window was to some extent the soul of the room and as its appearance changed, it would profoundly change the mood inside. Munch drew several sketches in various media, charcoal, pen, tempera, oil, and he very effectively rendered the variations in light, the grey, rainy weather in the morning of Act I, the mist in the afternoon and evening in Act II when it gradually grows darker and a lamp on the central table gives an eerie light until there is a faint red glow of fire through the window. In Act III the scene is dark in the night until the dawn and final sunrise makes the mountain peaks and glacier gleam through the window as Osvald sits with his back to the view and says, 'Mother give me the sun.' Munch faithfully recreated the atmosphere and changed very little in Reinhardt's plan, only moving the grandfather clock into the corner and placing one of the fireside chairs in a dominant position in the centre foreground in most of the sketches (cat. 78).

Reinhardt wanted Munch to provide first some sketches giving the colours and details of the furnishings, wallpaper, windows, and to send later some sketches to indicate the mood and shifts of light which would be helpful during rehearsals. He wrote:

> Up to now Ibsen's stage interior has been shockingly neglected and abused. However I believe that it constitutes an essential part of the **multiplicity** which lies between and behind Ibsen's words and which not only surrounds the action but also symbolizes it.
>
> I am firmly convinced that with your particular help we will be able to adjust the people and scenery to each other and to set them off in such a way, that we will illuminate as yet unfathomed depths in this splendid work and will accomplish a worthwhile task.
>
> Up to now the German stage has driven a more or less successful clinical study of insanity into the harsh footlights and has left the impression of everything else in the shadows. The **reverse** is in my opinion what is right. (cat. 77).

Reinhardt was very pleased with the pictures Munch eventually sent, and he was particularly impressed by the colours, which he thought would put the actors and the audience in the right mood. Munch's sketches were used for study in rehearsal and 15 of them were exhibited at the time of the performance. He attended some of the final rehearsals and the party to celebrate the success of the play.

Munch later continued to sketch some illustrations for **Ghosts** and in 1920 he adapted two of his earlier illustrations into lithographs, **Family Scene** and **Osvald** (cat. 74, 76). In **Family Scene** the ominous shadows thrown on the wall create the mood of the play without any fine details of scenery, and in **Osvald** Munch concentrated on the gestures of helplessness and despair (ill.29). The tragic juxtaposition of mother and child are reminiscent here of Munch's painting **The Sick Child**, although Osvald is turned away from his mother. The position of the figures in the illustrations for **Ghosts** indicate a great loneliness and lack of contact between people.

In later life Munch wrote that his 'Frieze of Life' expressed the mood of Osvald in **Ghosts**, that of a young painter who longed for the joy of life but was doomed by the biological determinism of a tainted inheritance. The longing for the sun outside the windows of dark, sad rooms was a recurring image in Munch's œuvre, but unlike Osvald, Munch broke out of the claustrophobic interiors and actually painted **The Sun** in his Oslo University Festival Hall murals in 1909-11. His paintings of bathers, and of people working in orchards, in forests and

29. **Osvald** (from Ibsen's **Ghosts**), 1920, lithograph OKK G/t 421

in grain fields expressed the sense of well-being in nature which his literary associates tended to confine to visions of an energy and fertility denied to most of their characters. In 1907 Munch included some paintings expressing a willing acceptance of nature in the 'Reinhardt Frieze', which decorated a gala room in the same 'Kammerspieltheater' in Berlin for which he designed the **Ghosts** and **Hedda Gabler** scenery. The coastline of Aasgaardstrand here provides the unifying background for 12 delicate panels which vary the images on the cycle of love which Munch had developed in the 1890s (cat. 81).

HEDDA GABLER, PEER GYNT AND JOHN GABRIEL BORKMAN

30. **Anitra's Dance** (from Ibsen's **Peer Gynt**), c.1913, crayon 35 x 26 cm. OKK T 1645

In Berlin in 1906 Munch was also commissioned to provide the décor for a performance of **Hedda Gabler** under the direction of Hermann Bahr. Munch attended rehearsals for the play and, with the help of friends, provided some furnishings from Norway for Hedda's living room. His finest sketch for the play is not however of the scenery, but of Hedda, standing alone beside a curtain, grim, tight-lipped and with her arms stiffly at her sides. Bahr did not ask Munch to suggest the mood of the play, as Reinhardt had done, nevertheless in the drawing of Hedda he indicated the frustration and isolation of Ibsen's character (cat. 79).

Reinhardt appears to have wanted Munch to provide illustrations for other plays by Ibsen. In a letter of 1909, Munch wrote to Reinhardt, 'I have often thought of our plans – sketches for Peer Gynt – Rosmersholm and other plays by Ibsen. Wonderful motifs – Perhaps I may yet do some of them.' (OKK MS) Although there was no further collaboration between Munch and Reinhardt, Munch did the majority of his illustrations of Ibsen's plays from about 1913 to 1930. In 1913 he drew variations of Anitra's dance in **Peer Gynt** (cat. 82), which in their spontaneity and gaiety mark a strong contrast to the symbolist illustration of Solveig and Aase for the Théâtre de l'Oeuvre in 1896. In about 1930 he drew some sketches of Aase's death; in one he placed Peer on the bed with his back to his mother, as in Ibsen's stage directions, and in another he showed Peer standing behind the bed. Munch expressed the sad old woman's features in a few lines and the dramatic force of Peer's fantasies by his free gestures and by the vivid shadows behind him (cat. 89).

Munch had known Ibsen when he wrote **John Gabriel Borkman** and he had drawn the theatre advertisement for its French première on 8 November 1897. (cat. 66) All his later illustrations for the play are free adaptations of scenes out in the snow, some of them only reported in the play, like the horse drawn sledge which carries off the young people and leaves Foldal hurt on the roadside. In the play it is a covered sledge drawn by two horses, but Munch simply transferred an earlier picture of a galloping horse into the landscape with snow-patterned fir trees which was characteristic of his drawings of **John Gabriel Borkman**. (cat. 83).

Munch drew a number of sketches called **Starry Night** which refer to the final scene in the play in which Borkman dies on a bench in the cold winter night, and he adapted one for a lithograph (cat. 67). The last act of the play appears to have impressed Munch most, and in his drawings he adapted the view from his own house in Ekely, ignoring Ibsen's stage directions of mountain ranges in the distance. Munch however conveyed by the light, stars and distant activity something of the visionary quality in Borkman's description of the steamships on the fjord: 'they come and they go. They create a world-wide sense of community. They bring light and warmth to the hearts of men in thousands of homes. That was what I dreamed of achieving' (cat. 90). It was perhaps this line which inspired Munch in 1897 to draw a lighthouse in the theatre advertisement for the play, in which he appears to have associated Ibsen with a power to illuminate the darkness.

31. After the Battle of Laaka, 1916-17, woodcut OKK G/t 661

THE PRETENDERS

One of Ibsen's early, lesser known plays, **The Pretenders**, inspired some of Munch's most powerful woodcuts. He was thoroughly familiar with the source material for this historical play and indeed it was one of his uncles, Peter Andreas Munch, who stimulated Ibsen's interest in the thirteenth century saga of the rivalry for the kingship of Norway, which provides the action of **The Pretenders**. Munch may also have been asked to illustrate the same historical material in Haakon Haakonson's saga for Stenersen's publishing house. During the First World War he did a series of drawings and woodcuts which refer to the saga. When he illustrated the scenes of destruction or flight, as in **After the Battle of Laaka**, he appears to have been making a reference to the horror of the **First World War** (ill.31).

In his woodcut **The Ordeal**, Munch in 1930 illustrated a scene from the saga which Ibsen used for the opening of his play **The Pretenders**. (ill.32) Here Inga shows her hands after she has undergone the trial of holding glowing hot iron to prove the royal parentage of her young son Haakon. The saga tells that Inga's hands were more beautiful after she had carried the iron than before, and Ibsen lets voices in the crowd remark on this when she first appears. Munch's main emphasis is on the figure of Inga after her ordeal. Her face looks emaciated and both the saga and the play tell that she had fasted beforehand. The faces that peer at her are shadowy and lightly outlined, and Munch let the grain of the wood show on the print to give the effect of transparency (cat. 70).

In his woodcut **Bishop Nikolas' Death**, the faces of the frontal figures appear like ghosts, while the hooked nose and long chin of the bishop give a caricature of an evil man. Ibsen suggested that Nikolas was in league with the devil even before his death, and the Bishop's scheming cruelty is brilliantly projected in the death scene in Act III of the play. Munch's illustration refers to the Bishop's repeated complaint that he cannot see, but that he has visions. Once again, Munch could adapt earlier scenes of his own to evoke the sensation of illness. Nikolas sits in profile, as do **The Sick Child** and **Osvald**, but the bishop has no sympathetic relative to help him. (cat. 68)

Munch's illustrations of Ibsen's play probably give a better insight into the tensions and psychological depth in many of the characters than any other artist who was faced with the same task. Gordon Craig found it difficult to make **The Pretenders** theatrically effective in 1926 when he was invited to design sets for a production at the Royal Theatre, Copenhagen. Munch in contrast found the daemonic scenes particularly fruitful for dramatic illustrations. He was less interested in the self-confident, successful Haakon than in the more tragic characters, and he did a particularly good illustration of a scene which

32. **The Ordeal** (from Ibsen's **The Pretenders**), c.1930, woodcut OKK G/t 657

William Archer called 'the great and flagrant artistic blemish of the Ghost Scene in the last act . . . a sheer excrescence on the play.'[25] In ironic verse, Ibsen there lets the ghost of Bishop Nikolas tempt Skule in the Elgeseter Wood. The ghost promises Skule the crown if he kills his grandson and has as his successor his own illegitimate son Peter, a priest. Ibsen's stage directions are a pinewood in a misty night, which Munch simply leaves to the woodgrain background in his woodcut, and he avoids the features which might seem melodramatic on the stage, like the red comet shining through the mist and the theatrical ghost dressed as a monk. The ghost appears in Munch's print as the Bishop's face, which has some resemblance to a skull, and Duke Skule's face on the left beside him. Both of them appear shadowy apparitions. (ill.33)

33. **Skule and Nikolas in the Elgeseter Wood** (from Ibsen's **The Pretenders**) 1916/17, woodcut OKK G/t 665

CONCLUSION

In a life-span of eighty-one years, Munch explored many styles and held more exhibitions than any of his contemporaries. His competence and mastery of his subject is evident from the energetic pace of his artistic experiments and exhibitions. He succeeded in creating compelling images and in responding in his own idiom to the art which he admired. His favourites among writers were Jaeger, Ibsen, Obstfelder, Strindberg, Nietzsche, Dostoevsky, Poe.

Munch made lasting friends and was receptive to other people. He remained on good terms with most of his early supporters for life and kept them in mind when he outlived them, producing portraits of Jaeger, Ibsen and Dauthendey after they had died. Even if it was only a copy of an earlier drawing or painting, he obviously wanted to remind himself of friends he had admired and liked. His portraits were considered by some critics to be the best part of his art.

Munch adapted his observations and record of his life into texts and pictures, for which he at times used literary models. An extract from one of his ledgers indicates just how close he was to the experimental self-analysis so characteristic of early modern writers:

> When I write these notes with drawings – it is not in order to tell about my own life – To me it is a question of studying certain hereditary phenomena that determine the life and fate of a human being – Just like phenomena indicating insanity in general. It is a study of the soul, I have since I practically can study myself – use myself as an anatomical soul preparation. But since it in the main is to create a work of art and a study of the soul, I have altered and exaggerated – and have used others for the studies – It is thus wrong to look upon these notes as a confession. I therefore divide – like Søren Kierkegaard – the work in two parts – the painter and his neurotic friend the poet.[26]

Munch was one of the greatest painters to create 'a work of art and a study of the soul.' His concern with the soul had been nurtured in a pietist home and stimulated further by his association with writers who aimed to express inner depth. With a few concise lines and colours, he could make the viewer aware of human joys, fears and trials, as well as virtues and vices. In spite of his famous **Scream**, his pictures frequently give a softer and quieter impression than the books by writers whom he considered his friends and rivals. His successful combination of a visual and more literary expression of psychological awareness does not limit his power as an artist but illustrates his versatility.

Carla Lathe

ABBREVIATIONS

OKK Oslo Kommunes Kunstsamlinger = Oslo Municipal Art Collections (Munch Museum)

OUB Oslo Universitetsbibliotek = Oslo University Library

Brev = **Edvard Munchs Brev: Familien** (Edvard Munch's Letters to his Family), selected by Inger Munch, Oslo, 1949

FOOTNOTES

1. Quoted by R. Stenersen, **Edvard Munch, Nærbilde av et geni**, Oslo 1964, p. 92.

2. See J. Thiis, **Edvard Munch og hans Samtid**, Oslo 1933, p.61.

3. **Das Werk des Edvard Munch**, Berlin 1894, p.37.

4. 'Det ene fornødne i Kunsten,' **Kunstbladet**, Copenhagen 1888.

5. Dr. Relling, **Die Kunst für Alle**, 15 May 1893.

6. **Barmer Zeitung**, 10 June 1893, no.134.

7. Dauthendey could not find a German publisher, and his book was translated into Swedish by Gustav Uddgren, who published it together with Dauthendey as **Verdensaltet. Det nye sublime i kunsten, Oversættelse**, Copenhagen 1893.

8. See B. Torjusen, 'The Mirror', note 18, Catalogue to the Edvard Munch exhibition, National Gallery of Art, Washington 1978.

9. **Frankfurter Zeitung**, 2.3.1927, no.245, reprinted in **Grundstoff der Bilder**, Munich 1959, p.178.

10. Quoted by K.E. Schreiner, **Edvard Munch som vi kjente ham. Vennene forteller**, Oslo 1946, p.6.

11. 'Zum schwarzen Ferkel,' signed 'W', **Neues Wiener Tageblatt**, 15 June 1901.

12. Letter in the Peter Hille Archive, Dortmund Stadt- und Landesbibliothek.

13. Quoted by S. Sawicki, 'Stanislaw Przybyszewski und Norwegen', **Edda**, 1934, p.14.

14. Letter from E. Goett, 29.10,1896, in the Dehmel Archive, Hamburg Staats- und Universitätsbibliothek.

15. A. Wysocki, **Sprzd Pol Wieku**, Krakow 1956, part 2.

16. Quoted by W.A. Berendsohn, 'Strindberg och Nietzsche', **Samfundet Örebro Stads- och Länsbiblioteks Vänner**, Meddelande XVI, 1948, p.18.

17. 'Nietzsche's Influence on Swedish Literature,' **Göteborgs Kungl. Vetenskaps- och Vitterhets Samhälles Handlingar**, no.3, 1956, p.24.

18. Undated letter in Thiel Gallery, quoted by G. Svenæus, **Oslo Kommunes Kunstsamlinger Årbok**, Oslo 1963, p.25.

19. Quoted by H. Fett, **Kunst på arbeidsplassen**, Oslo 1946, p.82.

20. For a full account of Munch's time in Paris, see B. Torjusen, 'The Mirror', op.cit.

21. 'The Bounty of Sweden,' **Autobiographies**, 1926, reprinted in London 1961, p.539.

22. Concerning Munch's illness, see A. Eggum, 'Hill i Munch-Museet,' Catalogue to the Carl Friedrich Hill exhibition, Munch Museum 1979.

23. Quoted by P. Hougen, **Farge på Trykk**, Munch Museum catalogue no. 5, 1968, p.6. Mary Sandbach kindly helped to translate the text into English for this catalogue.

24. 'Peer Gynt in Paris', 21.11.1896, reprinted in **Henrik Ibsen, A Critical Anthology**, ed. J.W. McFarlane, Penguin Books 1970.

25. Quoted by J.W. McFarlane, **The Oxford Ibsen**, vol.2, London 1962, p.25.

26. Quoted by G. Woll, 'The Tree of Knowledge of Good and Evil', Catalogue to the Edvard Munch exhibition, National Gallery of Art, Washington 1978, p.236.

BIBLIOGRAPHY

A. Brenna, 'Hans Jaeger og Edvard Munch', I and II, Nordisk Tidskrift, 52, 1976.

P. Gauguin, **Grafikeren Edvard Munch**, Trondheim 1946.

R. Heller, 'The Affaire Munch,' **Papers from the Xth AICA Congress at the Munch Museum**, Oslo 1969.

R. Heller, 'Edvard Munch's "Night", the aesthetics of decadence and the content of biography', **Arts magazine**, 53, no.2, 1978.

The Oxford Ibsen, 8 vols, ed. J.W. McFarlane, London 1960-77.

C. Krohg, **Kampen for Tilværelsen**, ed. Johan Borgen, Oslo 1954.

I. Langaard, **Edvard Munch, Modningsår**, Oslo 1960.

J. Langaard and R. Revold, **A Year by Year Record of Edvard Munch**, Oslo 1961.

C. Lathe, The Group Zum schwarzen Ferkel: a study in early modernism, (unpublished Ph.D. thesis, University of East Anglia, 1972).

C. Lathe, 'Edvard Munch and the concept of psychic naturalism', **Gazette des Beaux Arts**, 93, 1979.

H.B. Muller, Edvard Munch: A Bibliography, **Oslo Kommunes Kunstsamlinger Årbok, 1946-1951**, Oslo 1951.

Edvard Munch, Probleme – Forschungen – Thesen, edited by H. Bock and G. Busch, Munich 1973.

S. Przybyszewski, **Erinnerungen an das literarische Berlin**, translated from the Polish by K. Staemmler, Munich 1965.

G. Schiefler, **Verzeichnis des graphischen Werks des Edvard Munchs bis 1906** (Berlin 1907) and **Edvard Munch, das graphische Werk 1906-1926** (Berlin 1927); reprinted Oslo 1974.

R. Stang, **Edvard Munch**, translated by G. Culverwell, London 1979.

A. Strindberg, **Brev**, 13 vols, ed. T. Eklund, Stockholm 1965 ff.

G. Svenæus, **Edvard Munch: im männlichen Gehirn**, 2 vols, Lund 1973.

W. Timm, **The Graphic Art of Edvard Munch**, trans. Ruth Michaelis-Jena with Patrick Murray, London 1969.

O. Thue, **Christian Krohg. En Bibliografi**, Oslo 1968.

O. Thue, **Christian Krohgs Portretter**, Oslo 1971.

CATALOGUES TO MUNCH EXHIBITIONS

The Epstein Collection, Allen Memorial Art Museum Bulletin, Oberlin College, 29, no.3, 1972

Munch und Ibsen, Kunsthaus Zurich, 1976

The Sarah Campbell Blaffer Gallery, University of Houston, 1976

Edvard Munch: The Major Graphics, Smithsonian Institution Travelling Exhibition, Washington 1976

Liljevalch's Art Gallery and Kulturhuset, Stockholm 1977, (text in Swedish and English)

Edvard Munch, Der Lebensfries für Max Reinhardts Kammerspiele, Nationalgalerie, Berlin 1979

National Gallery of Art, Washington 1978

Die Brücke – Edvard Munch, Malmö Konsthall, 1979, (text in Norwegian, Swedish and German)

Frederick Delius and Edvard Munch, Munch Museum 1979, (text in Norwegian and English)

BRIEF CHRONOLOGY OF MUNCH AND HIS LITERARY ASSOCIATES

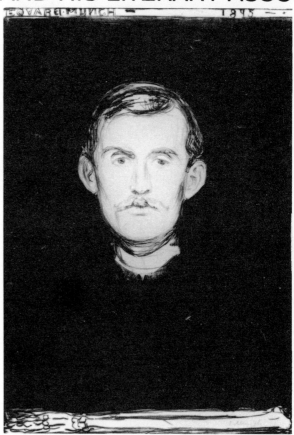

1880   Max Klinger dedicates his print series 'Eve and the Future' to Christian Krohg.

1881   Munch enters the School of Design in Oslo. Ibsen publishes **Ghosts**.

1882   Munch is supervised by Krohg; publishes a booklet with illustrated jokes.

1883   Munch first participates in annual autumn exhibition, favourable review from Gunnar Heiberg.

1884   Meets the group of bohemians led by Jaeger.

1885   Pays first brief visit to Paris. Jaeger's **From the Christiania Bohême** is confiscated.

1886 Exhibits **The Sick Child**. Krohg publishes **Albertine**, Ibsen, **Rosmersholm**.

1888 April-May Georg Brandes lectures on Nietzsche in Copenhagen. Munch exhibits 3 paintings in Copenhagen in summer.

1889 Strindberg opens experimental theatre in Copenhagen. April, Munch holds first one-man exhibition in Oslo (110 works). Is godfather to Krohg's first child, Per. Wins state scholarship for study abroad, attends Bonnat's art school in Paris for 3 months. Shuns social contact in the shock following his father's death.

1890 Vilhelm Krag and Jens Thiis introduce neo-romanticism in the Oslo Student Society.

1892 Munch draws vignettes for volumes of poems by E. Goldstein, V. Krag and S. Obstfelder; sketches and paints **Despair**. Holds one-man exhibition in Oslo, shows it in Berlin, where it causes a schism in the Artists' Association.

1893 Strindberg's **A Madman's Manifesto** is published anonymously in German in May, Dehmel's **But Love** in August, and Przybyszewski's **Requiem Mass**. December, Munch exhibits 6 paintings as 'Study for a series: Love' in Berlin.

1894 Przybyszewski publishes the first book on Munch's art. May, Meier-Graefe, Bierbaum, Dehmel and von Bodenhausen found the association **Pan**. Heiberg publishes **The Balcony**. Munch paints **The Woman in 3 Stages, Anxiety, Ashes, Red and White**.

1895 Meier-Graefe publishes a portfolio with 8 of Munch's first engravings. October, Munch exhibition in Oslo, visited by Ibsen, reviewed by T. Natanson in **La Revue Blanche**, and occasion for lecture by Obstfelder.

1896 Munch's engraving of Hamsun printed in **Pan**. Obstfelder's article on Munch is published in **Samtiden**. Munch draws illustrations for Baudelaire's **Flowers of Evil**. Prints colour lithographs and woodcuts with Clot. Dehmel publishes **Woman and World**, Ibsen **John Gabriel Borkman**, Obstfelder **The Cross**.

1897 Przybyszewski, **On the Paths of the Soul** and **Children of Satan** (dedicated to Munch), Strindberg, **Inferno**.

1898 Munch draws illustrations to accompany Strindberg's texts in the **Quickborn** journal.

1900 Obstfelder and Nietzsche die. Munch paints **Golgatha, Virginia Creeper, Dance of Life**.

1901 Dagny Przybyszewski is murdered by a lover. Munch prints etching **The Dead Lovers**.

1902 Munch exhibits his **Frieze of Life** in the Berlin Secession. After his affair with Tulla Larsen is terminated, he mostly avoids Norway until 1909, and distrusts former friends.

1904 **Das neue Magazin** publishes prints by Munch in its Strindberg and Peter Hille issues. Meier-Graefe publishes his 'History of the Development of Modern Art', includes Munch.

1906 Ernest Thiel commissions Nietzsche portrait. Reinhardt commissions designs for décor for Ibsen's **Ghosts**; Munch also begins sketches for **Hedda Gabler** décor.

1907 Munch completes **Reinhardt Frieze** for the Kammerspieltheater. Strindberg writes plays for the Intimate Theatre in Stockholm.

1908 Goldstein gets Munch into a clinic in Copenhagen for a nervous breakdown and alcoholism.

1909 Munch returns to settle in Norway. Publishes **Alpha and Omega**.

1910 Meier-Graefe publishes a book on van Gogh.

1911 Munch wins competition to decorate Oslo University Festival Hall.

1916 Munch begins to do woodcuts for Ibsen's **The Pretenders**.

1920 Lithographs of scenes in Ibsen's **John Gabriel Borkman** and **Ghosts**.

1929 Munch organizes his literary material.

c.1930 Illustrates Ibsen's **The Pretenders** and works on project for **Worker Frieze**.

1943-4 Munch's last print is a lithograph of Jaeger.

OUTLINE OF MUNCH'S LITERARY ASSOCIATES

DAUTHENDEY, Max (German, 1867-1918), writer who met Munch in Berlin and published a poem on the painting **A Vision**. He praised Munch as a pioneer of 'intimate art' in his book **Universe, the new sublime in art**, in 1893. Munch drew portraits of Dauthendey and of his Swedish wife, who knew Obstfelder, Vigeland, Tulla Larsen and many other Scandinavian writers and artists.

Drachmann 1901. lithograph

DRACHMANN, Holger (Danish, 1846-1908), writer whom Munch knew well in Berlin in 1893, and who encouraged Munch to be a rebel (cat.17). Drachmann flouted conventional behaviour, notably in his many love affairs. Although he cannot be confined to any particular literary movement, his novel **Confiscated** (1890) was a breakthrough for neo-romanticism. Drachmann was musically gifted, wrote libretti for operettas and was a leading figure in the cabaret movement at the turn of the century.

Goldstein 1908-9, lithograph

GOLDSTEIN, Emanuel (Danish, 1862-1921), poet whom Munch met in Paris in 1889 and with whom he planned to publish a journal for literature and art. Munch drew portraits of Goldstein in 1906 and 1908-9.

Hamsun 1896.

HAMSUN, Knut (Norwegian, 1859-1952), writer whom Munch met in Oslo and Paris. Hamsun did not sit for Munch's portrait of him and did not want it printed in **Pan** in 1896. The friction between them was aggravated by their poverty in the 1890s, but their appreciation of each other grew in later life. Hamsun's psychological novels in the 1890s were among the best of the period, and he won the Nobel prize for his novel **The Growth of the Soil**, 1917.

Heiberg 1896.

HEIBERG, Gunnar (Norwegian, 1857-1929), critic and dramatist who had known Ibsen and J.P. Jacobsen in Rome in 1878, and who admired Hans Jaeger. Munch and Heiberg were frequently together in the early 1890s and Heiberg introduced Munch to the group 'At the Black Piglet' in Berlin. After the end of Munch's liaison with Tulla Larsen, Heiberg was one of her circle who became a target for Munch's satire. Heiberg continued to like Munch's art.

IBSEN, Henrik (Norwegian, 1828-1906), dramatist who met Munch in the early 1890s. Munch drew theatre advertisements for Ibsen's premières at the Paris Théâtre de l'Oeuvre, and designed stage décor for performances of **Ghosts** and **Hedda Gabler** at the Berlin Kammerspieltheater.

JAEGER, Hans (Norwegian, 1854-1910), anarchist leader of the radicals in Oslo and the most ruthless advocate of free love. Wrote a book on Kant's philosophy in 1878. On account of his novel **From the Christiania Bohême** (1885) he was sentenced to prison, lost his post as parliamentary stenographer and was no longer allowed to attend the university, where he had studied philosophy part-time. In 1886 he wrote a review of Munch's **Sick Child** and described the painting **Hulda** which Munch had given him to hang in his prison cell.

KRAG, Vilhelm (Norwegian, 1871-1933), writer whose portrait Munch drew in pastels in 1891 and in a lithograph in 1920. Krag published poems in 1891 and prose poems written as monologues in 1892, which were typical of neo-romanticism. He printed poems inspired by Munch's paintings **Night** and **Despair** and was often together with Munch in Norway in the early 1890s. Krag hoped to include vignettes by Munch in the second edition of his poems (1894).

KROHG, Christian (Norwegian, 1852-1925), painter and writer who supervised Munch's painting and recommended him for at least 3 scholarships in the 1880s. Krohg in 1888 dedicated to Klinger his story **A Duel** (based on a literary fragment which Klinger had begun to illustrate in 1877). Krohg was a friend of Jaeger's and incurred the wrath of Bjørnson and other Establishment figures by editing pamphlets in protest against the confiscation of Jaeger's book in 1885. Krohg contributed reviews to Norwegian and Danish newspapers 1889-1924 and wrote appreciative articles about Munch until 1902. He published interviews with many of Munch's friends and painted their portraits.

MALLARMÉ, Stéphane (French, 1842-1898), leading symbolist poet of his time and friend of several impressionist and post-impressionist painters. Munch may have met him through his contact with writers who contributed to **La Revue Blanche** and **Le Mercure de France**. Munch shared Mallarmé's admiration for E.A. Poe. Although the lithograph and engraving Munch did of Mallarmé were probably based on a photograph, Mallarmé thought that Munch had achieved a penetrating likeness.

34. C. Krohg, **A Corner of my Studio**, 1885, oil, Lillehammer Art Gallery

MEIER-GRAEFE, Julius (German, 1867-1935), an engineering student who became an influential art critic. In 1894 he contributed an essay to **The Work of Edvard Munch**, and Munch painted his portrait. Meier-Graefe was one of the founders of the association **Pan** in 1894 and made contact with many artists for this project, including Toulouse-Lautrec. He helped Munch to arrange for his pictures to be exhibited in Paris and Brussels in 1896 and 1897. Organized the publications of the Marées-Gesellschaft, for which he in 1917 invited Munch to illustrate a character by Shakespeare.

OBSTFELDER, Sigbjørn (Norwegian, 1866-1900), writer who gave Munch hand-written copies of some of his poems. Munch planned to draw vignettes for Obstfelder's poems in 1892. In 1893 Obstfelder wrote an article on Munch, published in 1896 in **Samtiden**.

PRZYBYSZEWSKI, Stanislaw (Polish, 1868-1927), writer, pianist and student of medicine in Berlin. Editor of **Gazeta Robotnicza** (Workers' Gazette), 1892-3. Munch provided a sketch of the model for **Madonna** for the cover of the first edition of Przybyszewski's story **Vigils** in 1895. Through Munch, Przybyszewski met his Norwegian wife Dagny Juel, and the couple made Munch's art known in Poland when they moved to Krakow in 1898.

RODE, Helge (Danish, 1870-1937), poet and dramatist who joined the Christiania Bohemians in 1880s. Munch did portraits of him in 1891, 1898 and 1908-9. Rode was a spokesman for the anti-rationalist movement, was interested in Nietzsche's philosophy and in theosophy.

STRINDBERG, August (Swedish, 1849-1912), writer, whose novels and plays Munch knew well. Munch illustrated some of Strindberg's writing for the **Quickborn** magazine, 1899. They were together in Berlin 1892-3 and in Paris in 1896. Strindberg had written art reviews since the 1870s and painted some almost abstract pictures when Munch knew him. Munch was at times impressed by, at times sceptical about, Strindberg's interest in occultism and pseudo-scientific research.

CATALOGUE

Measurements are given in centimetres
OKK = Oslo Kommunes Kunstsamlinger (Munch Museum)

MUNCH, EDVARD (1863-1944)
1. Christiania Bohême I. 1895
Etching and drypoint 22 x 30.2. OKK G/r 9

KROHG, CHRISTIAN (1852-1925)
2. A Corner of my Studio. 1885
Oil, 56 x 67. Lillehammer Art Gallery
Photograph

KROHG, CHRISTIAN
3. Tredie Generation (Third Generation)
Verdens Gang, 27 April 1889
Munch is not like anyone else...He paints, or rather **sees** differently from other artists...Let us allow that he drew what is inessential badly, but he hits the mark on what is essential, both in the drawing and in the colour...He is an Impressionist, at present our only one!
Photograph

MUNCH, EDVARD
4. Self-portrait with Skeleton Arm. 1895
Lithograph, 46 x 31.5. OKK G/l 192

MUNCH, EDVARD
5. Hans Jaeger. 1896
Lithograph, 46 x 31.5. OKK G/l 218

ANONYMOUS
6. Bohembud (Commandments for the Bohemians)
Impressionisten, no.8, February 1889
'1. You shall write your autobiography. 2. You shall sever your family roots. 3. You cannot treat your parents badly enough. 4. You shall never slay your neighbour for less than five crowns. 5. You shall hate and despise all peasants like Bjørnstjerne Bjørnson, Kristof-fer Kristo-fersen and Kolbenstvedt. 6. You shall never wear celluloid cuffs. 7. Never fail to create a scandal in the Christiania theatre. 8. You shall never repent. 9. You **shall** take your own life.'
Photograph

MUNCH, EDVARD
7. Study for Melancholy
India Ink, 1891, OKK T 2355
Photograph

KROHG, CHRISTIAN
8. Munch
Verdens Gang, 27 November 1891
'The latest slogan now is 'sound' in colour. Has anyone heard such sound in colour, as in this picture . . . No ties – no tradition – no bridge – no influence. It may be that this is nearer to music than it is to painting, but it is at any rate brilliant music . . . [Munch] is the only one, the first, to turn to Idealism, who dares to make Nature, the model etc. subject to the mood and to alter them in order to achieve more.'
Photograph

MUNCH, EDVARD
9. Melancholy. The Yellow Boat, 1891-2
Oil, 65 x 96. National Gallery, Oslo
Photograph

MUNCH, EDVARD
10. Melancholy. 1896
Woodcut, 41.2 x 45.5 OKK G/t 571

MUNCH, EDVARD
11. Moonlight. Night in Saint Cloud. 1895
Drypoint and aquatint, 31 x 25.4. OKK G/r 12
The painting of the same subject dates from 1890; the figure by the window was the Danish poet Emanuel Goldstein.

MUNCH, EDVARD
12. Emanuel Goldstein. 1908-9
Lithograph, 27.5 x 24.5. OKK G/I 272

GOLDSTEIN, EMANUEL (1862-1921)
13. Poems 'Alruner' (Mandragoras), 'Vækst' (Growth) and 'Minder' (Memories), 1886
Alruner, Psykologiske Digte (Mandragoras, Psychological Poems), Copenhagen, 1916, 3rd edition.
Munch designed a frontispiece showing a variation of his drawing **Melancholy** for the second edition of these poems in 1892 (see cat. 23)
Photographs

MUNCH, EDVARD
14. Sigbjørn Obstfelder. 1896
Lithograph, 36 x 27.5. OKK G/I 220

MUNCH, EDVARD
15. The Scream. 1895
Lithograph, 35.5 x 25.2. OKK G/I 193

MUNCH, EDVARD
16. Holger Drachmann. 1901
Lithograph, 58.6 x 45.2. OKK G/I 240

DRACHMANN, HOLGER (1846-1908)
17. Berliner-Breve (Letters from Berlin)
Politiken, 24 May 1894
Photograph

MUNCH, EDVARD
18. Woman. The Sphinx. 1899
Lithograph, 46.2 x 59.2. OKK G/I 238

MUNCH, EDVARD
19. Gunnar Heiberg. 1896
Coloured lithograph, 48.9 x 42.2. OKK G/I 217

JAEGER, HANS (1854-1910)
20. **Fra Kristiania Bohêmen** (From the Christiania Bohême). 1885
Facsimile, Oslo 1976, 2 vols.

KROHG, CHRISTIAN
21. **Albertine,** 1886
Oslo 1976

MUNCH, EDVARD
22. Moonlight. Night in Saint Cloud. 1893
Pastel, 80 x 75. Private Collection
Photograph

GOLDSTEIN, EMANUEL
23. **Alruner, Psykologiske Digte** (Mandragoras, Psychological Poems)
Copenhagen, 1916, 3rd edition
Goldstein first published the poems under the pseudonym Hugo Falck as **Vekselspillet, Psykologiske Digte** (The Interplay, Psychological Poems) in 1886. Munch liked the poems and Goldstein dedicated the second edition to Munch, who provided the frontispiece.

MUNCH, EDVARD
24. Sphinx. The Woman in Three Stages. 1894
Oil, 164 x 250. Rasmus Meyer's Collection, Bergen
Reproduction

MUNCH, EDVARD
25. Catalogue to exhibition in Stockholm Konstföreningens Lokal, 1894
For entry 62. **Sphinx** (The Woman in Three Stages), Munch quoted a passage from Gunnar Heiberg's **The Balcony.**
Photograph

HEIBERG, GUNNAR (1857-1929)
26. **Balkonen** (The Balcony)
Copenhagen, 1894
Written in Berlin in 1893 and first performed with great success in Copenhagen on 1

January 1894. Krohg wrote about the dress rehearsal and première in **Verdens Gang**, 6
February 1894.

MUNCH, EDVARD
27a. Knut Hamsun
Pan, 1896, no. 1, facing page 173
Heliograph of drypoint engraving

DOUDELET, CHARLES
27b. Vignettes for poem by M. Maeterlinck
Pan, 1895, no.1
Photograph

WEISS, EMIL
27c. Vignettes for poem by H. von Hofmannsthal
Pan, 1895, no.1
Photograph

BIERBAUM, OTTO JULIUS (1865-1910)
28. 'Die Kranke' (The Invalid), poem inspired by Munch's engraving
The Sick Child.
Gesammelte Werke, Munich 1922, vol.1

MUNCH, EDVARD
29. The Sick Child. 1894
Drypoint with roulette, 35.7 x 27.1. OKK G/r 7

MUNCH, EDVARD
30. Girl in a Nightdress at the Window. 1894
Drypoint, 20.1 x 14.3. OKK G/r 5

MUNCH, EDVARD
31. The Day After. 1895
Drypoint and aquatint, 21 x 29.8. OKK G/r 14

MUNCH, EDVARD
32. Tête-à-Tête. 1895
Etching, aquatint and drypoint, 22 x 33. OKK G/r 11

MUNCH, EDVARD
33. The Lonely Ones, Two People. 1895
Drypoint, 15.5 x 21.3. OKK G/r 19

MUNCH, EDVARD
34. Dr. Max Asch. 1895
Drypoint engraving, 24.5 x 17.3. OKK G/r 26
Max Asch was a doctor who befriended many young painters and writers in Berlin. He
was nicknamed 'The Persian' for his looks. Asch discussed Nietzsche and Stirner with
Przybyszewski, found Strindberg a publisher in Berlin, and helped Munch to re-open
independently in December 1892 the exhibition which the Association of Berlin Artists
had closed.

MUNCH, EDVARD
35. Friedrich Nietzsche. 1906
Lithograph, 61.9 x 46.5. OKK G/l 263

MUNCH, EDVARD
36. Anxiety. 1896
Coloured lithograph, 42 x 38.5. OKK G/l 204

MUNCH, EDVARD
37. Stanislaw Przybyszewski. 1898
Lithograph, 54.2 x 44.1. OKK G/l 231

MUNCH, EDVARD
38. Mein Freund Przybyszewski (My friend Przybyszewski)
Pologne Littéraire, 15 December 1928
Photograph

MUNCH, EDVARD
39. Virginia Creeper. 1900
Oil, 119.5 x 121. OKK M 503
Reproduction

MUNCH, EDVARD
40. The Voice. Summer Night. 1896
Coloured woodcut, 37.7 x 57. OKK G/t 572

MUNCH, EDVARD
41. The Kiss. 1897-8
Woodcut, 59.3 x 46. OKK G/t 577-580

MUNCH, EDVARD
42. Vampire. 1896
Coloured lithograph and woodcut, 38.2 x 55.5. OKK G/t 567

MUNCH, EDVARD
43. Madonna. 1895-1902
Coloured lithograph, 60 x 44. OKK G/l 194

STRINDBERG, AUGUST (1849-1912)
44. L'exposition d'Edward Munch (Edvard Munch's exhibition)
La Revue Blanche, 1 June 1896
Photograph

DELIUS, FREDERICK (1862-1934)
45. Recollections of Strindberg
The Sackbut, 1 December 1920
Photograph

MUNCH, EDVARD
46. August Strindberg. 1896
Lithograph, 61.1 x 46.2. OKK G/l 219a

MUNCH, EDVARD
47. Jealousy II. 1896
Lithograph, 47.5 x 57.5. OKK G/l 202

MUNCH, EDVARD
48. Stéphane Mallarmé. 1896
Lithograph, 52.3 x 30.5. OKK G/l 221

MUNCH, EDVARD
49. Attraction I. 1896
Lithograph, 47.2 x 35.5. OKK G/l 207

MUNCH, EDVARD
50. Separation I. 1896
Lithograph, 48.8 x 58.5. OKK G/l 209

MUNCH, EDVARD
51. Separation II. 1896
Hand coloured lithograph, 44.1 x 62. OKK G/l 210-6
Poster

MUNCH, EDVARD
52. The Kiss by the Window. 1892
Oil, 72 x 91. National Gallery, Oslo
Reproduction

MUNCH, EDVARD
53. The Girl and Death. 1893
Oil, 128 x 86. OKK M 49
Reproduction

MUNCH, EDVARD
54. The Girl and Death. 1894
Drypoint, 30.2 x 22. OKK G/r 3
Photograph

PRZYBYSZEWSKI, STANISLAW (1868-1927)
55. Psychischer Naturalismus (Psychic Naturalism)
Neue deutsche Rundschau, February 1894

PRZYBYSZEWSKI, STANISLAW
56. **Auf den Wegen der Seele.**
Berlin, 1897

DEHMEL, RICHARD (1863-1920)
57. **Weib und Welt** (Woman and World)
Berlin, 1896

MUNCH, EDVARD
58. Designs to illustrate C. Baudelaire's **Les Fleurs du Mal** (1857)
Sketch for 'Une Charogne' (Carrion) OKK T 403 and for 'Le Mort Joyeux' (Gladly Dead)

OKK T 402. 1896
Photographs
Poems translated by Francis Duke, **The Flowers of Evil**, University of Virginia Press, 1961

NIETZSCHE, FRIEDRICH (1844-1900)
59. **Also sprach Zarathustra** (Thus spake Zarathustra)
Leipzig, 1897

STRINDBERG – MUNCH ISSUE OF QUICKBORN, 1899
60. Munch's illustrations **Harpy** and **Kiss of Death** for Strindberg's play **Simoom**; landscapes by Munch to illustrate Strindberg's short stories **The Silverswamp** and **Up to the Sun.**

STRINDBERG, AUGUST
61. Extract from MS of **Le Plaidoyer d'un Fou**, 1887-8
Oslo University Library, formerly in Munch's possession.
Photograph
Translated by Anthony Swerling as **A Madman's Manifesto**, Alabama University Press, 1971

MUNCH, EDVARD
62. Death of Marat. 1907
Oil, 151 x 148. OKK M 4
Reproduction

MUNCH, EDVARD
63. Death in the Sick Room. 1896
Lithograph, 40 x 54. OKK G/l 215

MUNCH, EDVARD
64. Two Women on the Shore. 1898
Coloured woodcut, 45.5 x 51. OKK G/t 589

MUNCH AND IBSEN

MUNCH, EDVARD
65. Advertisement for Ibsen's **Peer Gynt**, printed in 'La Critique', 20 April 1896
Lithograph 25 x 29.8. OKK G/l 216
Photograph

MUNCH, EDVARD
66. Advertisement for Ibsen's **John Gabriel Borkman**, printed in 'L'Art et la Scène', 1897
Lithograph, 21 x 32, 1902, OKK G/l 721

MUNCH, EDVARD
67. Starry Night (from **John Gabriel Borkman**). c.1920
Lithograph, 40.3 x 37.3. OKK G/l 497

MUNCH, EDVARD
68. Bishop Nikolas' Death (from Ibsen's **The Pretenders**). c. 1917-1920
Woodcut, 56 x 36. OKK G/t 669

MUNCH, EDVARD
69. Skule and Nikolas in the Elgeseter Wood (from **The Pretenders**). 1916-17
Woodcut, 28.2 x 52.7. OKK G/t 665

MUNCH, EDVARD
70. The Ordeal. Trial by Fire (from **The Pretenders**). c.1930
Woodcut, 45.8 x 37.3. OKK G/t 657

MUNCH, EDVARD
71. Ibsen in the Café of the Grand Hotel. 1902
Lithograph, 43.5 x 59. Taken from a drawing 1897, OKK G/l 244

MUNCH, EDVARD
72. Ibsen in the Grand Café. 1906-1910 (?)
Tempera, 115.5 x 180.5. OKK M 717
Photograph

MUNCH, EDVARD
73. A scene from Ibsen's **Ghosts**. 1906
Tempera, 60 x 102. OKK M 983
From left to right: Osvald, Mrs. Alving, Pastor Manders, Engstrand, Regine
Photograph

MUNCH, EDVARD
74. Family Scene (from **Ghosts**). 1920
Lithograph, 42 x 64.5. OKK G/l 420

MUNCH, EDVARD
75. Illustration of Osvald's breakdown in **Ghosts**. 1906
Tempera, 71 x 90. OKK M 1037
Photograph

MUNCH, EDVARD
76. Osvald (from **Ghosts**). 1920
Lithograph, 40 x 50. OKK G/l 421

REINHARDT, MAX (1873-1943)
77. Notes to Munch on stage décor for Ibsen's **Ghosts**. 1906
Munch Museum MS
Photograph

MUNCH, EDVARD
78. Stage sets for **Ghosts**. 1906
Tempera and crayon, Munch Museum and Bergen Municipal Collections
Photographs

MUNCH, EDVARD
79. Stage sets for Ibsen's **Hedda Gabler**. 1907
Sketches in charcoal, tempera and water colour, Munch Museum
Photographs

KAHANE, ARTHUR (1872-1932)
80. Edvard Munch
Berliner Tageblatt, 28 October 1926
Article on Munch's work for Reinhardt's commissions
Photograph

MUNCH, EDVARD
81. Desire, for **Reinhardt Frieze** in the Berlin Kammerspieltheater. 1907
Section of painting in tempera, 91 x 250, National Gallery, Berlin
Poster

MUNCH, EDVARD
82. Anitra's Dance (from Ibsen's **Peer Gynt**). c.1913
Pencil and crayon drawings, Munch Museum
Photographs

MUNCH, EDVARD
83. Illustrations for Ibsen's **John Gabriel Borkman**. 1916-1923
Charcoal drawings, Munch Museum
Photographs

MUNCH, EDVARD
84. Illustrations for The Saga of Haakon Haakonson and Ibsen's **The Pretenders**. 1916-1921
Woodcuts, Munch Museum
Photographs

MUNCH, EDVARD
85. Illustration for Ibsen's **When we dead awaken**. 1912-18
Ink, OKK T 2420
Photograph

MUNCH, EDVARD
86. Letter to Dr. Julius Elias (? 1895)
Oslo University Library MS, Brevs. 166
Photograph

MUNCH, EDVARD
87 Reminiscences of Ibsen
Munch Museum MS
Photographs

MUNCH, EDVARD
88. **Livsfrisens tilblivelse** (The Origin of the Frieze of Life) Oslo, c.1929
Munch published this booklet of extracts from his diaries and other notations in about

1929, when he organized his literary material. He wrote about his memory of Ibsen's comments when he visited the Munch exhibition which caused a public outcry in Oslo in 1895. Ibsen said, 'believe me – you will fare the same as I did – the more enemies, the more friends.' (p.13)

MUNCH, EDVARD
89. Aase's Death (from Ibsen's **Peer Gynt**). c.1930
Two drawings in Munch Museum, reproduced in the Catalogue to the 'Munch und Ibsen' exhibition at the Kunsthaus, Zurich, 1976

IBSEN, HENRIK (1828-1906)
90. **Peer Gynt** (1867), **John Gabriel Borkman** (1896), **The Pretenders** (1863) and **Ghosts** (1881)
Translations from **The Oxford Ibsen**, edited by J.W. McFarlane London 1961-77
Photographs

LITERARY CONTRIBUTIONS AND REACTIONS TO MUNCH'S ART

MUNCH, EDVARD
91. Max Dauthendey
Lithograph, 1924, from drawing c.1897, OKK G/l 441
Photograph

DAUTHENDEY, MAX (1867-1918)
92. 'Vision', poem inspired by Munch's painting **Vision**
Blätter für die Kunst, 1893, part 3
Photograph

MUNCH, EDVARD
93. Vision. 1892
Oil, 72 x 45. OKK M 114
Reproduction

MUNCH, EDVARD
94. Study for vignette as title page for **Digte** (Poems). 1892
Sketchbook, OKK T 129 p.21
This drawing of a girl gazing at a sun or moon over the sea was probably intended for an edition of Vilhelm Krag's poems.
Photograph

OBSTFELDER, SIGBJORN
95. 'Jeg ser' (I see), poem from his **Digte** (Poems), 1893
Samlede Skrifter, Oslo 1950, vol.1
This poem was written in the summer of 1892, when Munch and Obstfelder were often together. Obstfelder wrote to his brother, c.25 July 1892, 'I received a letter from Vilhelm Krag yesterday. His publisher wants to produce my poems by Christmas – the painter Edvard Munch wants to draw one or more vignettes –' S. Obstfelder, **Breve til hans Bror**, ed. S. Tunold, Stavanger 1949
Photograph

MUNCH, EDVARD
96. Study for vignettes. 1892
Sketchbook, OKK T 129-38
These sketches are similar in composition to the paintings **Despair** and **The Scream**. 'He thought that he had drawn 'The Scream' after he had read Obstfelder's poem 'Surely I have come to the wrong planet' [I see].' Rolf Stenersen, **Edvard Munch, Nærbilde av et geni**, Oslo 1964, p.92
Photograph

MUNCH, EDVARD
97. Study for Despair. 1892
Charcoal and oil, OKK T 2367
In the margin Munch wrote, 'I was walking along the road with two friends – the sun set. The sky suddenly turned blood red (and I felt a breath of melancholy – a pain sucking at my heart). I stopped, leant against the railing dead tired – above the blue black fjord and town lay blood and tongues of fire. My friends went on and I stood still, trembling with fear – and I felt a great unending cry through Nature.'
Photograph

MUNCH, EDVARD
98. Despair. 1892
Oil, 92 x 67. Thiel Gallery, Stockholm
Photograph

KRAG, VILHELM (1871-1933)
99. Text til Edvard Munchs maleri 'Stemning ved Solnedgang' (poem inspired by Munch's painting **Despair**)
Dagbladet, 19 September 1892
Krag merges his impression of Munch's paintings **Despair** and **Night in Saint Cloud**, and ends his poem, 'Deep into the night I sat alone. / I felt an anguished scream / resound over the godforsaken world.'
Photograph

MUNCH, EDVARD
100. The Scream. 1893
Oil, pastel and casein, 91 x 73.5. National Gallery, Oslo
Reproduction

NATANSON, THADÉE (1868-1951)
101. Correspondance de Kristiania
La Revue Blanche, no.59, November 1895
Natanson wrote this article after seeing Munch's exhibition in 1895. 'He deserves full credit for not refraining in any way or in any painting from what one is forced to assume is always the search to achieve something different, something new. However, one is inclined to deplore the fact that he, perhaps satisfied with the degree of perfection to which he had attained, neglects somewhat the pictorial emotions in order to express mainly those which are human ... But it is not going too far to take heed of Mr. Munch's poetic turn of mind and of his taste for literature.'
Photographs

THOMPSON, VANCE (1863-1925)
102. Munch, the Norse Artist
M'lle (New York) vol.l, no.10, January 1896

'The journals of Kristiania assert that he offends public morality. His pictures are refused admittance to the galleries. I have seen many of his pictures, it is true, which should not be shown to young girls. It would be a trifle absurd, however, to confine art within the limit of the young person's imagination./ If you can imagine Rowlandson blended with Puvis de Chavannes in equal proportions you will have a fair idea of Edvard Munch.'
Photograph

KROHG, CHRISTIAN
103. Portrait of Gunnar Heiberg by C. Krohg and lithograph of **The Scream** and accompanying text by Munch printed on pp. 527-8
La Revue Blanche, December 1895
Photographs

MUNCH, EDVARD
104. Mystic Shore, 1892
Oil, 100 x 140. Private Collection
Photograph

SCHEERBART, PAUL (1863-1915)
105. Munch und Gallén
Adels- und Salonblatt, III, no.24, 1895
Review of exhibition in Berlin, March 1895. 'It is Munch's intimate relation with literature which makes him so incomprehensible to the wider public. He could have expressed most of what he began to paint rather better with words. Much would then have developed into a poem – some would have developed into an aesthetic discourse.'
Photograph

MUNCH, EDVARD
106. Fever. 1893
Pastel, 59 x 78.5. OKK M 121
Photograph

MUNCH, EDVARD
107. Self-Portrait with Cigarette. 1894-5
Oil, 110.5 x 85.5. National Gallery, Oslo
Photograph

UNIVERSITY OF OSLO LIBRARY
108. Minutes of Obstfelder's lecture on Munch and ensuing debate in the Student Society, 9 November 1895
Obstfelder compared Munch with Rembrandt, remarking that their self-portraits were similar, that Rembrandt worked with shadows, Munch with dark colours. After the lecture, the painter Hans Heyerdahl said that Munch had nothing in common with Rembrandt, but had learnt from Böcklin's use of blue.
Photographs

MUNCH, EDVARD
109. Madonna. c.1894
Oil, 90 x 68.5. OKK M 68
Poster

GÉRARD, EDOUARD
110. Le Peintre Ed. Munch
Munch Museum MS of article printed in **La Presse**, May 1897
Munch reprinted Gérard's article in exhibition catalogues in 1897 and 1918.

MUNCH, EDVARD
111. Red and White. c.1894
Oil, 93 x 107. OKK M 460
Poster

MUNCH, EDVARD
112. Livsfrisen (The Frieze of Life)
Tidens Tegn, 15 October 1918
In this article Munch first gave the name 'The Frieze of Life' to pictures which had occupied him since the 1880s. 'The same mood content in the various areas of the Frieze issued directly from the struggles of the 1880s and forms a reaction to the rampant realism then. The Frieze is conceived as a series of decorative pictures, which together should give a picture of life . . . The Frieze is thought to be like a poem about life, about love and death.'
Photographs

HAMSUN, KNUT (1859-1952)
113. Edvard Munch
Aftenposten, 25 January 1944
Following Munch's death on 23 January 1944, the newspaper **Aftenposten** asked Knut Hamsun to write a few commemorative words about Munch. He immediately sent this short poem.
Photograph